THE ENTROPIC PHILOSOPHY

THE ENTROPIC PHILOSOPHY

Stevie Kaschke

www.steviekaschke.com

ISBN: 978-1-7371211-0-7 (print)
ISBN: 978-1-7371211-1-4 (ebook)
ISNB: 978-1-7371211-2-1 (audio)

First Edition: May 2021

Illustrations, and interior layout by Tyler Kaschke
Cover design by Jeff Lenger

For Tyler

Without your help, love, and support this book would have
never been written.

Contents

Introduction

ORIGINAL THOUGHT EXPERIMENTS are at the core of this book. Thought experiments about the multiverse, biological life, and consciousness are discussed in chapters two, three, and four, respectively. But the discerning reader should pick up on one last thought experiment that isn't spelled out in a single chapter. Even though this thought experiment doesn't have its own chapter, it's the most important one in the book.

For thousands of years, philosophers have been asking existential questions and trying to make sense of our existence. There are lots of theories about the meaning of life, but none have stuck. Our quest for meaning and purpose ended abruptly at existentialism. Existential philosophy teaches that your life is a blank slate and the only meaning and purpose your life has is what you give it yourself. Most existentialists think that any continued search for greater shared meaning is absurd.

As someone who came to philosophy searching for answers and meaning in my own life, it's still hard for me to believe that our collective search for meaning has stopped here. Existentialism doesn't just feel unsatisfying, it feels arrogant. With the view of history, we can now look back on existentialism differently. Instead of taking these ideas so literally, we could now look at existentialism as arising in the mid-1800s when we knew much less about ourselves, our world, and our universe. We can look at the original existentialist philosophers as frustrated intellectuals who didn't have any answers back then and postulated that if they don't have answers, then maybe that's just because there aren't any.

This entire book is dedicated to exploring a single idea in detail – what if life does have a definite purpose? What if that purpose was something we could use our scientific knowledge to understand and even quantify our progress towards?

This is the thought experiment that spans the entire length of this book, and it's the one that should be taken the most seriously. The smaller thought experiments about entropy, the multiverse, life, and consciousness, haven't yet been vetted by thorough academic peer review. I have talked with some subject matter experts individually, but until a broader scientific community weighs in on these thought experiments, it's reasonable to retain skepticism about the entropic philosophy in general.

While the smaller thought experiments need further review, the main thought experiment in this book is ready. It just needs your review and your ultimate decision. After reading this book, does a continued search for meaning still seem absurd and pointless? Do you still think we'll never know why we're here and what we should do about it? These are the questions I hope my thought experiment can help you answer for yourself.

While I do think we desperately need fresh answers to our questions (the topic of chapter one), the point of this book is not to convince the reader to start practicing the entropic philosophy. The point of this book is to show us that a search for meaning has merit and that we shouldn't stop searching. A unifying philosophy, one that can give us common goals and meaning, continues to be the most important intellectual pursuit of all. We have no reason to give up on that.

Part I

Thought Experiments

1

We Need a New Story

"WHY DOES CLIMATE change matter?" I recently posed this question to an environmental journalist who has dedicated their entire career to educating the public about problems related to climate change and conservation. Because of their passion and interest in this topic, we were both surprised when he didn't have a ready answer. After some prompting and discussion, the environmental journalist did provide an answer to my question.

"Climate change is wrong because it's causing many species of biological life to die."

"But why is this wrong?" I challenged. "Our planet has gone through five mass extinctions in the past. Were these also morally wrong? Is it only the sixth mass extinction, caused by humans, that's wrong?" We drilled down this line of questioning until we got to the philosophical root.

The answer we hit on was moral hedonism. The journalist feels that climate change and the current mass extinction are wrong because they cause him personal suffering. On the surface, this might seem like a selfish response, but understanding moral hedonism can help us understand that this is a reasonable place to end our philosophical inquiry. Hedonism gets a bad rap from its colloquial use to describe pleasure-seeking behaviors but hedonism is not synonymous with gluttony. For some, it's pleasurable to help the poor, save the planet, and sacrifice personal wants to help others. Hedonism is seeking whatever makes you happy and avoiding whatever makes you unhappy. For the environmental journalist, climate change was wrong because it made him unhappy to see both human and non-human life suffering from the effects of climate change.

The environmental journalist is not in bad company. Many prominent philosophers and philosophical movements throughout history can be classified under the umbrella of moral hedonism. This group includes Aristotle, Plato, the Buddha, and even Albert Einstein. These hedonists might say that climate change is wrong if it also caused them personal suffering.

Up until very recently, moral hedonism didn't look like such a bad option but now seems foolish juxtaposed against our newly acquired knowledge. Humanity's new knowledge of ourselves, our planet, and the universe have come to reveal how small and insignificant we are in this more complete schema. In an infinitely vast universe that's over 14 billion years old, on a planet that's over four billion years old, populated with an estimated nine million species other than *Homo sapiens* – How could it possibly be that human feelings are the supreme authority of right and wrong? This becomes even more apparent with our new knowledge of what human feelings are: a cascade of biochemical algorithms honed over time by evolution. With all that we know now, human emotions have come to look very small and insignificant in the grand scheme of reality.

But this is where the greatest thinkers in human history have left us. I remember reading an introductory philosophy text, *A Brief History of Human Thought*, which summarized all of western philosophy into 257 pages. Mostly I remember being extremely disappointed by the end of the book. It started well enough by explaining key concepts of western philosophy in ancient Greece where the philosophy of stoicism dominated for some time. Christianity then replaced stoicism as the dominant worldview for hundreds of years. It wasn't until the 1700s that non-religious philosophy came back in vogue during the enlightenment. The philosophy of humanism, a type of moral hedonism, was born from the enlightenment. A few hundred years later, philosophers like Nietzsche dismantled both humanism and religion as illogical and even harmful ideas. There has been little meaningful work since Nietzsche left us staring into the gaping void of nihilism. Instead of jumping into the void, most of the world has chosen to stay in the 1700s instead. I don't blame anyone for doing this. Nihilism is a very disappointing ending to the history of human thought.

The world today is running a philosophical operating system written over 350 years ago by men who wore wigs and waistcoats and sported lace ruffles for extra style points. In the early 1700's we didn't know what atoms were, or that natural selection by evolution could explain the diversity of life on earth. We didn't know about thermodynamics, germ theory, or even genetics. Yet, we still deem the work of enlightenment era thinkers worthy to base a global society on.

This is how we find ourselves in the year 2021 with a global philosophy that hasn't caught up with the insights gleaned from Copernicus over 500 years ago[1]. Copernicus was the first person to reject the cosmic model depicting Earth at the center of the universe. Copernicus's insights sparked a revolutionary paradigm shift in human thinking – A paradigm marked by humility, curiosity, and a glimmer of understanding about our true place in the vast universe. This paradigm shift in thinking was foundational to the scientific revolution. Scientific inquiry is based on the notion that we humans have something left to learn; that we don't already have the answer for everything, and that humans, and our happiness, are not at the center of the universe. Philosophy seems to still be lagging behind the Copernican Revolution of the 1500s. Worldviews like humanism and religion still place humans and human feelings at the center of the universe.

...

---

[1] Immanuel Kant's ideas are said to be the Copernican revolution of philosophy, but this is inaccurate in terms of what Copernicus did for science in relation to what Kant did for philosophy. As important as Kant's work was to the enlightenment, his ideas ultimately ended up bolstering a case for humanism which still puts humans and our happiness as the supreme moral authority in the universe. It's also worth noting that Immanuel Kant is the one who said his ideas were like the Copernican revolution of philosophy. This was not something historians or later philosophers said about his work.

I remember a conversation with a fellow 5th grader about Santa Claus. It was November, and as much as I was looking forward to Christmas and presents, that year I was troubled by the approaching holiday. My main issue was that we didn't have a chimney in our house for Santa to enter through. I reasoned that since we didn't have a chimney, Santa would have to come in through one of the doors, but all our doors were always locked at night. I never remember my parents unlocking them on Christmas eve.

Even if Santa had some universal key, he'd still have to walk through our carpeted living room to get to our Christmas tree. Where I grew up, there was usually snow in December. This means Santa should have snow stuck to his boots which would leave behind wet carpet or even mud stains. I mused about how odd it was that my mom left out a Diet Coke for Santa when this was her favorite beverage, and I'd always heard that Santa preferred milk with his cookies. At this point, the other girl finally interrupted me and said. "It sounds like your parents haven't told you yet." She went on to break the news to me.

Just three years later when I was in eighth grade, these same sorts of questions started creeping into my religious faith. I was raised Catholic in my childhood – sitting in church every Sunday, attending special masses for feasts and holidays, going to Sunday school when I was young. I was even confirmed in the Catholic faith. My religion was a big part of my childhood. Unlike my Santa Claus story, I can't remember an exact moment that I stopped believing in God, but it was around this time in middle school that my skepticism began to outweigh what was left of my faith.

High School was the dark age for me philosophically speaking. I didn't put much thought into what should guide my life or provide meaning to my existence in the absence of religion. It wasn't until college that I thought more about these questions and found humanism. Humanism was an attractive philosophy to me for many reasons. It provided morals and ethics without religion and gave me a tribe again. The dictionary of Oxford Languages defines humanism as follows:

"Humanism is an outlook or system of thought attaching prime importance to human rather than divine or supernatural matters. Humanist beliefs stress the potential value and goodness of human beings, emphasize common human needs, and seek solely rational ways of solving human problems."

Humanism and I had a good run, but it wasn't long before this philosophy was stressed to its breaking point. After graduate school, I had an existential crisis precipitated by a failed business venture and the stress of adapting to life outside of school. I turned to humanism to help guide me morally, but humanism had no answers. Humanism only told me that it was good for me to be happy and good to make others happy, too. This wasn't very useful in helping me work through what weighed on me. This is how I got to moral nihilism – a philosophy that holds nothing as good or evil. Nothing is right or wrong and all morals are just a human construct that has little significance in the broader universe. Pretty heavy stuff to land on in your mid-twenties.

I looked around desperately for philosophical alternatives. I didn't like being a nihilist, but it was the only thing that made any sense. I looked into Buddhism, Stoicism, and Epicureanism as philosophical alternatives, but was let down. They were no different at their core than humanism was. All four of these philosophies are a form of moral hedonism – the view that human happiness is the supreme moral good. Moral hedonism was not helping me answer any of the questions I now had. It didn't help me understand why my life had meaning. It didn't help me understand what the goal of a human or a collective society should be.

I opened this chapter with the question "Why does climate change matter?" While this is a good question, it directs our focus away from the real problem.

Climate change isn't the problem.
Nuclear war isn't the problem.
Environmental destruction and pollution aren't the problems.

The real problem? We are teetering on the edge of philosophical bankruptcy. Our modern global society is running off the fumes of what the enlightenment era thinkers gave us.

For most of us, philosophy takes a back seat to commerce. And for those who aren't religious, capitalism is the philosophy that replaces nihilism (even if they aren't aware that this is the case). Often, we are so worried about making money and surviving that we lose sight of what this system is working towards. The frightening answer is that capitalism isn't working towards anything at all. There's no broader goal, no vision for the future, and no moral meaning to it. In this way, capitalists are just gussied up nihilists with wealth and social prestige to placate the philosophical void inside them.

Capitalism doesn't have answers for us either.

I'm not the only modern thinker who realizes this. Yuval Noah Harari is a philosopher, futurist, professor, and author of the New York Times Best Seller *Sapiens: A Brief History of humankind*. Harari has thought at length on the subject of human history, philosophy, and the future of mankind. To truly understand the scope of the problem – you need to understand how important philosophy, or stories as Harari puts it, have been to humankind. Stories are what enabled us to flourish and dominate our planet; they're what allowed us to become so distinct from any other animal on earth. Here's what Harari has to say about how our belief in things like gods, nations, money, and human rights help us cooperate with complete strangers:

"There are no gods in the universe, no nations, no money and no human rights—except in the common imagination of human beings. You can never convince a chimpanzee to give you a banana by promising him that after he dies, he will get limitless bananas in chimpanzee heaven. Only Sapiens can believe such stories. This is why we rule the world, and chimpanzees are locked up in zoos and research laboratories."

Without stories, like money, religion, and nations we humans are not able to function in networks beyond about 150 individuals. These stories are what allow us to cooperate today at a near-global scale in groups of millions and even billions.

Stories of our past helped us cooperate in tribes and disparate nations. But in our globalized society, all of them are failing. They have little or nothing to say about climate change or technology. Maybe worse is that we don't yet have a global story. Stories of our past have helped us cooperate in tribes and disparate nations. We now need to cooperate as one global society. Hedonism and nihilism won't do the job. If we have any hope of solving our global problems, we need a new story. The following thought experiment and philosophical theory are my best crack at storytelling.

Admittedly, my story isn't as easy to understand as others. It requires the reader to understand concepts like entropy, evolution, and astrophysics to understand the eventual moral of the story at the end. Even the most technically educated reader may still have questions after reading this (I have plenty of questions of my own left), but I hope the ideas are presented in a way that those of any educational background will understand what the entropic philosophy is and why it matters.

While the entropic philosophy pulls from technical fields, it's not just for technically trained people. We need more than just biologists and physicists on board to help us solve our global problems. We need everyone we can get. Ideally, we will eventually have global buy-in for our new global story. We need look no further than the problems of climate change and nuclear war to see why this is true.

This story may not be the one that ultimately gets global buy-in, but we need more people telling stories. The enlightenment era stories were written before humankind discovered concepts like thermodynamics, natural selection, or multiverse theory. The stage has been bereft of serious storytellers for 100s of years now. A new audience, armed with new knowledge and wisdom, is tired of hearing these same stale tales retold again and again. Our old stories have lost their luster after being put on display next to the twinkling jewels of 21st-century knowledge. Worse is that there's a growing faction that has no story at all. It's time for a new age of raconteurs to step on stage and use our new knowledge to captivate a modern audience.

Even if you find fault with this story, I ask that you embrace the spirit of this tale. This story is told with earnest humility as I search for my own meaning and purpose in life. To find a new global story, we must all go on a similar search and let go of superstition, egotism, and pride. There's a chance you may be lacking a story and don't realize it yet. Whether you already have your own story or not, I'm not asking that you take up my story as gospel, but I am asking that you keep an open mind.

Now, if you're ready, kick off your shoes, settle in and grab a cozy seat.

It's storytime.

Chapter Summary

- We're teetering on the verge of philosophical bankruptcy and almost all of our most pressing global problems stem from this greater issue.

- Religions, capitalism, and past philosophies don't provide compelling enough reasons for us to work together globally to solve issues like nuclear war, climate change, ecological collapse, or human suffering.

- To solve these problems we need a new philosophy (story) that will give us a common goal to work towards and help us thrive as a global community.

2

The Evolutionary Multiverse

IN THE BEGINNING, there was a singularity. About 13.8 billion years ago, all the matter and energy that comprise our universe was condensed together in an infinitely small dense point before exploding out in the big bang. This is how many astrophysics would begin the story of our cosmic genesis. While few scientists dispute the big bang theory of our universe's birth, there is a growing faction that says the dawn of existence pre-dates this event. This camp of astrophysicists includes accomplished scientists such as Steven Hawking, Neil DeGrasse Tyson, and Brian Green. These experts say we have to look beyond our universe to find the true inception of everything. We need to look to the multiverse.

The multiverse isn't an easy concept to wrap a human mind around. While astrophysicists agree on a definition for a multiverse; a multiverse is a collection of multiple individual universes, this definition is about all they agree on. Theoretical physicists have identified nine different "types" of multiverse that could exist. That is to say, nine different identified mechanisms that could result in the creation of multiple universes. The definition of a multiverse remains the same in all these nine different models. The explanation for how these multiple universes came to be is the part that changes.

The multiverse explanation gaining the most momentum in physics is called the inflationary multiverse. The inflationary model is the one that Steven Hawking, Neil DeGrasse Tyson, and Brian Green are proponents of. Inflationary cosmology is pretty well accepted now by astrophysicists. Astronomers have long observed the expansion of our universe. We can measure that galaxies and objects in space are moving away from us and each other and the speed at which objects are hurdling away is only increasing (see Figure 2.1).

This observation is the initial insight that led to the big bang theory. The logic that started the theory is simple. If everything is expanding apart, then in the past things must have been much closer together. The big bang theory says that our universe started as a densely packed singularity and then BANG, something happened. The matter and energy in the singularity exploded out and have been radiating and expanding faster and faster for billions of years. The big bang theory of our universe is now well-accepted in cosmology, partially owing to empirical data about cosmic background radiation that further backs it up. If this theory is right, it explains a lot about the nature of the universe – like how the different physical elements are distributed and how our universe

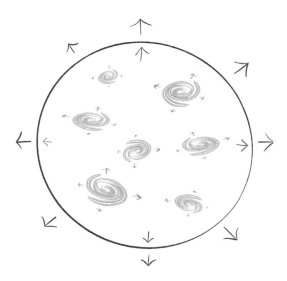

Figure 2.1: Galaxies in a universe moving away from each other. As the galaxies spread apart the universe also grows as everything pushes the boundaries of the universe out further.

seems to structure itself. Most notably, the big bang theory aligns with the Hubble-Lemaître law which is based on the observation that the further away a galaxy is from us, the faster it's moving away.

This is why the inflationary model of the multiverse is the most well-accepted. Inflationary cosmology is a critical component of the big bang theory. If it's true, as most scientists believe, that the universe started as a singularity and has been expanding for the past 14 billion years, then that means we live in a universe that is inflating and expanding.

There are two different ways an inflating universe can create multiple universes from inflation. If the rate of inflation is constant, then an inflating universe will create multiple "Hubble volumes" inside of itself where the space separating these volumes is so vast, that they are essentially separate from one another, even though they are contained inside the same expanding parent universe. The second way a multiverse can be created out of an expanding universe is if the rate of inflation is *variable*, not constant. This variable inflation, otherwise known as eternal inflation, is the one we'll be discussing in this chapter.

Physicist Alan Guth proposes that the rate of inflation in our universe is variable due to quantum fluctuations in the cosmological constant (the constant dictating how fast our universe expands). To understand how variable inflation can lead to a multiverse, a visual analogy might help. Think about a universe with variable inflation rates like a balloon being inflated, but some parts of the balloon wall are weaker than others. The parts of the balloon with weaker walls will inflate faster than the parts with thicker walls. The thin-walled parts of the balloon will pocket out and expand faster (as shown in Figure 2.2). This is key to understanding the eternal inflationary multiverse theory. Not all parts of the balloon are inflating at the same rate. Some parts are inflating extremely rapidly, while in other areas the balloon can stop inflating altogether. This disparity in inflation rate throughout the universe is what can lead to the creation of multiple universes.

Eventually, the parts that expand rapidly become spatially separated from each other to such an extent that they're considered to be "pocket universes" formed within the initial expanding

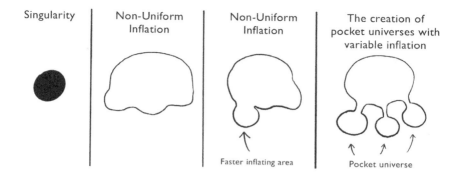

| Singularity | Non-Uniform Inflation | Non-Uniform Inflation | The creation of pocket universes with variable inflation |

Faster inflating area

Pocket universe

Figure 2.2: Starting from a singularity, the universe starts expanding into a 3D volume. Inflation occurs at different rates in different parts of the universe causing some areas to bulge and pocket out. After some time, areas of high inflation will be separated completely from areas that have low or no inflation, creating pocket universes.

volume. The creation of these pocket universes could go on infinitely into the future. That's because of something remarkable that falls out of this model. Intuitively we might expect inflation to slow down over time. If we push a ball down a hill, it rolls quickly for a while but then stops rolling eventually as all the potential is used up. Eternal inflation doesn't work the same way. Yes, inflation does slow down in some areas, but in the areas that are still inflating, the creation of new space far exceeds the decay of the inflationary rate. So even though the rate of inflation decays, what we end up observing is faster and faster inflation that could theoretically go on into infinity. This is how we end up with an infinite multiverse as a logical conclusion tied to inflationary cosmology.

We can't prove or disprove for sure that we live in a multiverse, but it does seem likely given what we know about the big bang and the inflation of our universe. Since we can't directly observe the multiverse or test it scientifically, this is an assumption the following thought experiment is based on. It's the only assumption, but it's a big one. Even though it's an assumption, it's grounded in evidence and logic. We do have reason to believe that we live in an inflationary multiverse. With this background, let's dive into the implications of what this all means.

Universes Pass on Heritable Traits to Offspring

My border collie looks nothing like what you'd expect and few people guess her breed correctly. The weirdest guess we've gotten is a beagle dalmatian mix. I'll let you decide if that's an apt description of our pup Risten or not (see Figure 2.3). I don't think our purebred border collie looks like a dalmatian or a beagle, but she definitely doesn't look like a "regular" border collie. She has smooth short hair when long rough hair is typical of her breed. Her coat has three colors: black, white, and brown. A typical border collie is only black and white. The last quirk is that her ears are pricked and upright. They don't flop down like the ears of a typical border collie. While these traits together aren't common in this breed, we know where they come from. Risten's mom also had short hair and pricked ears, and her dad had similar coat colorings. She inherited these physical traits from her parents.

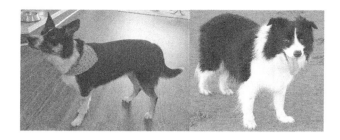

Figure 2.3: Pictured left: Our border collie, Risten. Pictured Right: A "regular" border collie (Wikimedia Commons).

The concept of heritable traits is a cornerstone of biology with all living organisms inheriting traits from their parents. If we live in a multiverse, then this same concept of heritable traits also applies to universes. In the eternal inflation model, a new universe would be born after essentially "budding" off from a parent universe. With this in mind, what's depicted in Figure 2.2 starts to look a whole lot like a-sexual reproduction with offspring budding directly off of parents.

Biologists have a name for inherited traits that are observable. My dog's smooth coat and pricked ears are called phenotypes. Other examples of phenotypes in humans would be blue eyes, curly hair, or freckles. We too inherit these traits from our parents. The mode through which we inherit traits is through our DNA, or as a biologist would say, our genotype. There are genes for blue eyes, curly hair, and pricked ears. These genes get passed on from parent to offspring and so on down the family tree. In biology, the genetic code of DNA serves as the mode through which heritable traits get passed onto offspring.

Universes don't need DNA to pass on traits to their offspring. Any form of matter or energy would fulfill this same purpose. In the inflationary model, matter and energy from the parent universe are being pinched off to form the budded offspring universe. Since both parent and offspring share the same matter and energy, it can be assumed that this matter and energy may serve as the hard coding for some type of heritable trait. One example of a heritable trait is the ratio of physical elements. Since matter and energy are inherited from the parent universe, it's reasonable to think that the ratio of different elements would be passed on from parent to offspring. Figure 2.4 visually explains this concept in more detail.

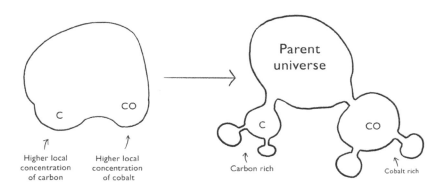

Figure 2.4: Elements may not be equally distributed in an expanding universe. One corner of this expanding universe has a higher local concentration of cobalt compared to the other corner which has a higher local concentration of carbon. When these corners bud off and become an offspring universe, they each have a different relative abundance of elements.

In this example, the relative abundance of physical elements could serve as the genotype that codes for different phenotypes. For example, a universe richer in hydrogen (genotype) might have a higher density of stars (phenotype). Another example is that a universe with the right ratio of hydrogen to carbon to nitrogen (genotype) might be better at producing biological life like what we see on Earth (phenotype).

There are other modalities for universes to pass on heritable traits to their offspring. The ratio of physical elements is just one example of how this could happen. Another example of a trait that could be inherited via matter and energy is the cosmological constant. As discussed earlier, this constant dictates a universe's rate of expansion. The rate of expansion or dark energy could also serve as coding material that results in different phenotypes in offspring universes. These are just three examples of how universes could pass on heritable traits to offspring, but the list of possibilities is much longer.

Random mutations in heritable traits occur

Our genes are under constant assault by our environment, microbes, and even our own bodies. The sun's rays, chemicals in cured meats, cigarette smoke, and even peanut butter are known agents that can cause genetic mutations. While there are lots of different mechanisms for how mutations can occur, at a basic level all genetic mutations have one thing in common. The mutated genetic sequence is different from the original sequence. For example, take an original strand of DNA that reads ABCDEFG. Hit this strand of DNA with enough sunlight and it could later read ABCXYGFE. The mutated strand carries a different message that changes how the genes are expressed in the organism.

Mutations can occur in the genotypes of universes, too. Figure 2.4 shows how it's possible to end up with offspring universes that have a different ratio of elements than the parent universe had. The example provided in figure 2.4 was offspring universes with different concentrations of cobalt and carbon. See Figure 2.5 for what could happen when the offspring universes keep expanding and bear offspring of their own.

The other example provided for a possible universe genotype, the rate of inflation, could also be prone to mutations. The eternal inflation model tells us that inflation can continue indefinitely. But how could this possibly be true? In physics, we expect things to slow or disperse as it moves down a gradient. When you push a shopping cart away from you it eventually slows to a stop. Inflation in a universe doesn't work this way. The rate of inflation is a quantum property. Without getting into the weeds too much about what this means – suffice to say that the physics of things on the quantum scale do not work the same way as shopping carts in a parking lot. According to the inflationary multiverse model, an offspring universe could have a higher rate of inflation than the parent. This is due to quantum fluctuations in inflationary speed. The quantum fluctuations are analogous to random mutations. When this quantum fluctuation occurs, it's random and is passed onto offspring. This, coupled with the fact that inflation outpaces decay, is what allows inflation in the multiverse to occur indefinitely.

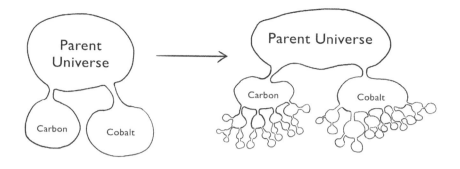

Figure 2.5: A parent universe can birth two offspring that have a different relative abundance of elements from the parent. In this example, the offspring are carbon-rich and cobalt-rich respectively relative to the elemental distribution of the parent. The carbon-rich universe could bear more offspring and the carbon could be further concentrated in resulting offspring relative to the grandparent.

When a universe dies, it can no longer reproduce.

When a human, a hummingbird, or a hemlock plant dies, none of these individual organisms are capable of reproduction any longer. The same is true for universes in an inflationary multiverse. What could possibly kill a universe? It turns out that the grim reaper is the same for all of us. Humans, hummingbirds, hemlock plants, and even universes all die at the hand of the same thing. Entropy will one day come for us all. To understand entropy's lethal power, we need a better understanding of not just entropy, but also free energy. This thought experiment is already dense enough, so I'll try to keep these definitions as simple as possible.

***Entropy**= Increasing disorder; entropy destroys gradients.*

***Free Energy**[2] = Concentrated gradients of ordered matter, temperature, or pressure*

This explanation is a good start, but we'll expand on it shortly (including a brief look at the math). Before diving into equations, these non-mathematical definitions are a good place to start.

Sharing a story might help make these definitions more clear. My husband and I recently bought our first home. Since the house wasn't maintained well, the home inspection process is something I paid close attention to and remember well. After a thorough assessment, the home inspector gave us a report. Out of 105 items inspected, 37 items needed maintenance, and 26 items needed repairs. The gutters had spots of rust, there was damage to the exterior trim, the driveway had cracked and become uneven, there was damage to parts of the drywall, and the exterior paint was fading in spots. Without proper attention, parts of the house had started to fall apart. What was once a thick coat of paint had been worn away with particles of the paint becoming more disordered as the elements dispersed them away into the environment. What was once solid wood trim had rotted and chipped in spots as the wood became more disordered in the process of decay and erosion.

------

[2] There are passages in this book where a better word to use instead of "free energy" would be "exergy". Instead of defining a new term and using both terms throughout the book, I chose to only use the term "free energy" even though I technically use this term incorrectly at times and should use the term "exergy" instead. Please note "entropy" as discussed in this book denotes thermodynamic entropy and not information entropy.

The driveway, which was once a single piece of concrete, had cracked and broken up into several distinct pieces that shifted independently with the soil. This is entropy (disorder) increasing.

We weren't shocked by the findings of this inspection. The second law of thermodynamics primed us on what to expect. This natural law dictates that entropy in the universe will always increase. This is exactly what we saw in the summary of our home inspection. The disorder of this home had increased in the 34 years since it was first built. Entropy doesn't just increase on private residential property – although many homeowners know well that it does. Smoke from a cigarette curls in the air before drifting away in the wind. Cream swirls in coffee before completely dispersing in the mug. A dropped wine glass shatters, but never spontaneously reforms from the broken pieces. These are all examples of ordered gradients of matter breaking apart as entropy increases.

If entropy is always increasing, then how could my husband and I ever hope to make the 26 home repairs the inspector found? How could we put this home back into a more ordered state? Entropy has a temporary antidote known as free energy. An important nuance to point out here is that *free energy* and *energy* are not the same thing. Energy can neither be created nor destroyed. Energy can be changed into different forms, but it is always conserved. Conversely, *free energy* can be irrevocably destroyed. Calling it free energy is a total misnomer because, unlike "regular" energy, free energy can get used up. Once we use up all the free energy in our universe, it's all gone. There's no getting it back.

Free energy is what my husband and I need to fix up our home. In our home improvement endeavors, we'll likely need some power tools. Free energy is required to produce the electricity needed to power these tools. Electricity is still mostly generated from burning fossil fuels. The highly ordered carbon-carbon bonds in fossil fuels are a form of free energy. When we break these bonds by burning fossil fuels, heat is created. In order to turn a turbine to generate electricity, this heat is sequestered in a neat and orderly pool. The hot molecules of steam are highly organized together and separated from the colder molecules of air (an ordered gradient of physical matter). Some of that heat escapes its ordered confinement as the turbine turns, yielding some of the order of hot molecules by letting those molecules mix with colder molecules. Entropy (disorder) increases and free energy (order) decreases. After all the hot molecules escape, there is no way to collect them and put them back in an ordered container. Ordered gradients of free energy are irrevocably lost.

So now we all understand entropy and free energy, but what does this have to do with a universe dying? The second law of thermodynamics can help answer this question for us. If entropy in the universe is always increasing, then one day the universe will reach maximum entropy. This means if entropy only increases, then there will come a day that entropy can't increase any further. All the ordered free energy in our universe would be completely used up. A universe that has reached maximum entropy, has reached maximum disorder. Physicists call this the eventual heat death of the universe. It's called the death of the universe because after maximum entropy is reached, no work can be done – Nothing can happen. All the ordered free energy in our universe that allows work to be done would be completely used up. Entropy is what kills a universe in the multiverse. When max entropy is reached, it means everything in the universe is at thermodynamic equilibrium. In other words, all physical gradients of matter in the universe have been broken down and max disorder has been reached.

An expanding universe creates more room for entropy to increase. To truly reach max entropy, the universe must stop expanding. If there are different rates of expansion in the universe, then that means that gradients of order are being produced as part of the universe balloons to infinity with the matter inside it spreading out. Relative to this highly expansive area, the matter in the rest of the universe would be comparatively condensed. This is a non-random gradient of matter. The condensed matter can diffuse into the less dense area where expansion is occurring rapidly. A universe that's expanding in a non-uniform way is creating gradients with its variable inflation. This means that a universe that has reached max entropy is no longer expanding. If expansion of the universe can occur after it has reached max entropy, then we live inside the very perpetual motion device that physics says should not exist.

It's for this reason that we should assume that when max entropy is reached in our universe, inflation has stopped. When inflation stops, that means the "dead" universe can no longer reproduce. Remember that in inflationary cosmology, the inflation of the universe is how budded offspring are created. If there is no more inflation, then there is no way for more offspring universes to bud off of the parent. To summarize, when a universe reaches max entropy that means inflation has ceased, which in turn means that the universe is no longer able to reproduce and bear more offspring.

Cosmological Natural Selection & The Black Hole Multiverse

While these may seem like novel ideas, I'm far from the first to assert that evolution by natural selection would apply to a multiverse. Physicist Lee Smolin published an entire book on this idea back in 1999. In his book, *The Life of the Cosmos*, Smolin explains his hypothesis about the multiverse. The central thesis of the book is that if we do live in a multiverse, the collapse of black holes could serve as the nucleus for the birth of a new universe. The new universe, born from the black hole of the parent, would inherit slightly mutated traits from the parent such as the Planck constant, or masses of elementary particles.

Smolin argues that in a multiverse that reproduces through black holes, there would be selective pressure for more black holes. The more black holes a universe has, the more offspring it has as these black holes eventually collapse. Therefore, traits that enable the creation of more black holes in a universe would be selected over time.

In his theory, Smolin cites the same universe assassin I do: Entropy. Smolin theorizes that universes created with non-ideal parameters will reach heat death before being able to reproduce. In this black hole model of reproduction, more black holes aren't all that would be selected for. If entropy "kills" a universe before it can bear offspring, traits that delay the heat death of the universe would also be selected. A topic we'll discuss in more detail in the next section.

While Smolin's ideas about black hole births have been met with a mixed reception from other physicists, his broader idea has garnered much interest from the field. This broader idea is known now as cosmological natural selection and it's caught the attention of physicists, evolutionary biologists, and even philosophers. Cosmological natural selection, or CNS as it's often referred to in academic papers, is the theory that if we live in a multiverse, then natural selection by evolution applies.

The thought experiment outlined in this chapter is a new idea that fits in the framework Smolin architected almost 30 years ago. Not only does this thought experiment work with an inflationary multiverse, but it also works with the black hole model of multiverse reproduction. In the next section, we'll see how all these ideas culminate to reveal what natural selection by evolution in a multiverse could be selecting for.

Natural Selection to Slow the Increase of Entropy

Darwin illustrated natural selection by describing variations in the beaks of finches he observed in the Galapagos Islands. A species of finch living on one island had a small slender beak, but on a different island, the finches had stout powerful beaks. Along with this observation of finch beak size, Darwin noticed that the food sources on the two islands were different. The finches with the long thin beaks had more insects to dine on, while the finches with the powerful stout beaks ate a diet of nuts and seeds. Darwin reasoned that the food source on each island provided a selective pressure that caused the different beak morphologies. On the nut and seed island, random mutations that resulted in a larger beak would mean those birds got more food because the larger beak could easily crack the nuts and seeds. If it got more food, it had a better chance of surviving and creating more offspring.

As Smolin suggests with his theory of cosmological natural selection, universes and finches aren't so different. Natural selection shapes the features of both. This thought experiment identifies lifespan as a selective pressure acting on a universe within an inflationary multiverse or black hole multiverse. The arrow of time flies forward as entropy increases and a universe ages towards heat death. Once a universe dies, it can no longer reproduce. Universes that live the longest would create the most offspring because they have the longest window of time open for reproduction. Universes where entropy increases rapidly would not live as long and therefore have a shorter timeframe available for reproduction. This means a long life is a trait that would be selected for and driven through the population. Figure 2.6 illustrates this concept.

In an inflationary multiverse and black hole multiverse, there's selective pressure for universes that live a long time. In order to keep inflating and creating offspring, there would be selective pressure to slow the increase of entropy. It's worth pointing out again that entropy can't *decrease*. The second law states that entropy will only continue to increase. It's not a violation of thermodynamic laws if entropy increases slower, as long as entropy still increases overall. Man and universe have this struggle with entropy in common and neither of us has been able to find a true fountain of youth. Not even natural selection in a multiverse can violate the laws of physics. When a universe runs out of ordered

A universe that has a long life has more time to produce offspring.

Universes that die young have less time to create offspring before they stop expanding.

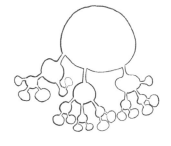

The longevity trait drives through a population.

The short lifespan trait does not get driven through a population.

Figure 2.6: The left image shows a universe with a long life span that can inflate for a long time before reaching heat death. The longer it's able to inflate, the more offspring it's able to produce. These offspring inherit the longevity trait from the parent and are also able to produce lots of offspring which also live for a long time. The right image shows a universe that will die young. This universe does not have much time to inflate and create offspring before reaching heat death. The short-life trait is passed on to the single offspring which also dies young and only has time to reproduce once before death. This trait does not get driven through a population. A short lifespan is not what would be selected for.

gradients (free energy), no more work can be done. Free energy is not renewable and once it runs out, it's gone for good.

If this thought experiment is correct, then we should see vestiges of entropy slowing systems in our universe – and we do. Scientists have found evidence supporting that entropy in our universe is increasing at the slowest rate possible. This is consistent with the work of 1977 Nobel Prize-winning chemist Ilya Prigogine who discovered that out of equilibrium systems will take on the configuration of forces and flows that minimize its rate of entropy production. Prigogine studied out of equilibrium chemical reactions and their resulting entropy production. The output of his experiments is now called the Minimum Entropy Production Principle (MINEP). As the name suggests, MINEP explains that entropy in a system will increase at the slowest rate possible.

Physicist Freeman Dyson studied this same topic on a much larger scale. In his 1971 publication *Energy in the Universe*, Dyson argues that the universe is creeping very slowly towards thermodynamic maximum. Dyson provides a rationale to help us understand how the universe is slowing itself down from reaching maximum entropy. The following is a quote from Dyson's publication:

"Since the universe is on a one-way slide toward a state of final death in which energy is maximally degraded, how does it manage, like King Charles, to take such an unconscionably long time a-dying?"

In his paper, Dyson explains that the universe employs several "hang-ups" that slow down the depletion of free energy in our universe. In his paper, Dyson cites six different ways the universe slows itself down from depleting available free energy. For example, he cites the fact that many celestial bodies are spinning as a hang-up. As long as an object is spinning rapidly or orbiting, it stops gravitational collapse. Spin is what stops our planet from being sucked into the sun. He also discussed a transport hang-up. According to Dyson, transport hang-ups "...*arise because the transport of energy by conduction or radiation from the hot interior of the earth or the sun to the cooler surface takes billions of years to complete. It is the transport hang-up that keeps the earth fluid and geologically active, giving us such phenomena as continental drift, earthquakes, volcanoes and mountain uplift.*"

There may be more hang-ups slowing the increase of entropy in our universe than what Dyson listed in 1971. In the next chapter, we'll take a look at a possible seventh and *vital* way our universe employs a hang-up that slows itself down from reaching max entropy.

Chapter Summary

- We likely live in a multiverse which means evolution by natural selection acts on individual universes.

- In the inflationary and black hole multiverse models, max entropy "kills" a universe and stops it from reproducing.

- In the inflationary and black hole multiverse models mechanisms that slow the increase in entropy would be selected to maximize lifespan and offspring production.

- There is evidence from physicists and chemists showing ways chemical systems and the larger universe slows itself down from reaching maximum entropy. This research supports the output of this thought experiment.

3

Life's Purpose in an Evolutionary Multiverse

I'M NOT THE only one with thought experiments about entropy. A thought experiment posed by physicist James Clerk Maxwell in the late1860's can help us better understand definitions of free energy, entropy, and out of equilibrium systems. In his thought experiment, Maxwell thought he had discovered a paradox that would cause a violation of the second law of thermodynamics; he thought he had discovered a way that entropy could *decrease*.

In this thought experiment, Maxwell envisioned a chamber filled with both hot and cold molecules bouncing around inside randomly. This chamber could be described as being at thermodynamic equilibrium, meaning there was no thermal gradient between the randomly distributed hot and cold molecules. In his thought experiment, Maxwell adds a dividing wall that splits the chamber in half and a demon that sits just outside this chamber controlling the door. This demon has the power to open the door to selectively let molecules through. The demon opens and closes this door as molecules randomly bounce around to selectively let hot molecules pass through and accumulate in the right chamber, and to let the cold molecules accumulate in the left chamber. The result is a statistically unlikely gradient of physical matter (hot and cold molecules) separated by a membrane. (See Figure 3.1)

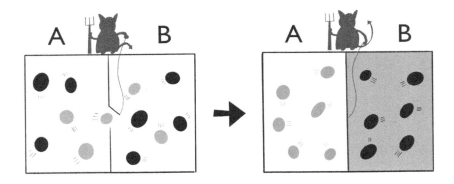

Figure 3.1: Left: a chamber with a dividing wall that is at thermodynamic equilibrium. The hot and cold molecules in this chamber are completely randomly dispersed. Right: A gradient of hot and cold molecules is created by Maxwell's demon. This gradient embodies free energy as the hot molecules can be released to mix with the cold molecules and work can be done as the free energy gradient is used up.

This thought experiment, called Maxwell's Demon, reveals no paradox in the laws of thermodynamics. Yes, the entropy of the chamber was decreased, but what Maxwell failed to see is that the demon was equivalent to an input of free energy to the system.

What would the demon eat to stay alive? How would it have perfect computational knowledge of the heat and trajectory of each molecule? These things take free energy. The demon itself is a form of free energy used to create an ordered gradient of hot and cold molecules.

Maxwell's chamber is an example of what's called an out of equilibrium system. Out of equilibrium systems have a constant influx of free energy going into the system that allows for ordered gradients of matter to be created. Non-equilibrium systems are so different from other systems, there's an entirely separate branch of thermodynamics that studies them. This field of physics is called non-equilibrium thermodynamics. We should all be very familiar with non-equilibrium systems. Almost everything we see in nature on Earth is a non-equilibrium system. A tornado, a lightning storm, biological life (including us), and the entire planet we live on are all examples of out of equilibrium systems.

What Maxwell didn't realize in 1867 was that he was living in the very chamber he imagined. We all live in a planet-shaped chamber with a constant influx of free energy coming from our sun. In our planet's chamber, biological life is the gradient-producing demon. Maxwell may not have realized this, but almost 150 years later biochemist Nick Lane came to understand this truth well. In his 2016 book called *The Vital Question: Energy, Evolution, and the Origins of Complex Life*, Nick Lane argues that gradients of protons are at the heart of life's origin. Lane argues that the laws of physics concerning entropy and free energy are the very reason why life arose on Earth. Lane and many others now profess that thermodynamic gradients, and not DNA, are what should define biological life at a molecular level.

Lane makes a compelling argument that illustrates how life could have first originated in deep ocean hydrothermal vents. To understand Lane's ideas, we need to understand ocean vents. The salient points to know are that some hydrothermal vents have pocked walls, called micro-pores. When certain molecules in these vents flow through they get caught in the microporous walls. This can cause molecular gradients to build up in certain areas up to 1200x the concentration in other parts of the vent. Not only does this lead to a molecular gradient in the vents, but due to the chemistry of the water, it also leads to a pH gradient.

Lane proposes that the first proto-cell was powered by naturally occurring pH gradients in these microporous vents. At first, these gradients were created by passive processes in the vents, but over time a more active process may have evolved. The first active proton pumps (like what we see in all biological cells), may have evolved in these vents to create ion gradients across a semipermeable membrane. In Maxwell's thought experiment, the demon created a gradient of molecules separated by a semipermeable membrane. This should now sound very familiar. The proton gradients that power all life on earth are statistically unlikely, and yet we see them in every living organism from a cyanobacterium to a crawdad. Figure 3.2 shows this proton gradient being created inside the membrane of a mitochondrion.

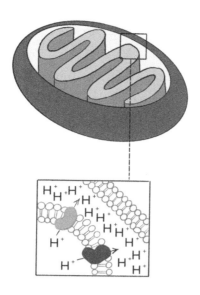

Figure 3.2: The proton gradient at the heart of life's complexity. Inside the mitochondria's membrane has a very low concentration of hydrogen ions (H+). Energy is used to pump ions across a membrane where there is a higher concentration of H+ ions. Maybe we should start calling it Maxwell's mitochondria.

This proton transport is what's responsible for driving the creation of adenosine-triphosphate (ATP) inside cells. ATP, sometimes called the currency of the cell, is a molecule that drives all of life's complexity. This molecule is a tiny token of free energy that gets spent to create the ordered gradients of complex life we see today. Proton gradients are what make statistically unlikely complex biological life possible. Without these proton gradients, life would never have evolved, and it wouldn't exist today. If there's life on one of the other 40 billion Earth-like planets in the Milky way, gradients of physical matter are sure to lie at the core of their existence as well.

These gradients of ordered physical matter are what mitochondria and Maxwell's demon have in common. In Maxwell's thought experiment the demon is the source of free energy that pumps hot molecules into one chamber and cold molecules into the other. In biology, the source of free energy is the sun[3]. The sun is the source of power that allows life to pump protons into different membranous chambers. Maxwell thought he had discovered a paradox that invalidated the second law of thermodynamics. He thought his chamber defied the laws of physics as the demon seemingly made entropy decrease. Maxwell did not discover a paradox. What he discovered free energy and out of equilibrium systems.

Is Life a Paradox?

At first glance, it might seem like life is at odds with the laws of thermodynamics. If entropy is always increasing, how do we end up with highly organized atoms that become animated biology? Life is anything but disordered and random. Plants for example grow out of random CO_2 and water molecules, but the resulting

---

[3] There is life on Earth that is powered by free energy that doesn't come from the sun. If the first life on earth did originate in the pores of a deep-sea vent, then it wasn't the sun that powered this. The naturally occurring pH gradients in the vents are in themselves a source of free energy. This is a very small source of free energy, but it was enough for life to get started before finding a much bigger source of free energy via the sun.

54

plant represents a highly complex gradient of physical matter. Carbon and nitrogen and hydrogen all lumped up together in ways that seem nearly impossible from a statistical or thermodynamic perspective. The feather of a bird, the branching veins on a leaf, and the bones inside a human body are all highly complex structures that were built out of disordered bits and pieces. *This is not how entropy is supposed to work.*

If you look just beyond our planet, the laws of physics come back into focus. The sun provides energy that makes life on earth possible. The random CO_2 and water that coalesces into the leaf of a plant do not violate the second law of thermodynamics. Just like Maxwell's demon, biological life is perfectly in line with the laws of thermodynamics. Even though a gradient of matter is being created in the form of a leaf, overall the entropy of the system is still increasing. The fireball of our sun is a hotbed of entropic increase. Some photons and free energy are released as entropy increases. Life siphons off some energy from the sun to create organized gradients via photosynthesis, but overall entropy is still increasing in this reaction. A new child can be born and a new tree planted, but despite all the organized gradients that comprise life, entropy still increases.

The Thermodynamics of Biology

If you don't count demons as part of life's taxonomy, then it wasn't until 1944 that someone first started thinking about the thermodynamics of biological life. Physicist Erwin Schrödinger didn't just theorize about cats in boxes. He spent a good chunk of his career exploring entropy and biology. In his book *What is life?*

Schrödinger examines biological life through the lens of physics. Through this examination, he concludes that life is very different from other matter in the universe in that it resists entropy's siren call of decay. Schrödinger does provide an answer to his question *What is life?* According to the physicist, Life feeds on "negative entropy" to avoid entropic decay. The following are some selected passages from chapter six of Schrödinger's book *What is life?*

- *"It is by avoiding the rapid decay into the inert state of 'equilibrium' that an organism appears so enigmatic."*
- *"How does the living organism avoid decay? The obvious answer is: By eating, drinking, breathing and (in the case of plants) assimilating."*
- *"What an organism feeds upon is negative entropy."*
- *"An organism's astonishing gift of concentrating a stream of order on itself and thus escaping the decay into atomic chaos – of drinking orderliness from a suitable environment."*

What Schrödinger calls "negative entropy" now has another name; it's known as free energy. Life uses free energy (initially supplied from the sun) to create the order and complexity we see all around us on our planet. In other words, life feeds on free energy to create complex gradients and avoid the decay of entropy.

After Schrödinger, many other physicists and biologists started thinking more about the thermodynamics of life. Much of the published literature similarly refers to biological life; referring to life as a low entropy system that uses free energy from the sun to organize itself into complex gradients. Lee Smolin for example has the following to say about biological life in his book *The Life of the Cosmos*:

"A living system... continually creates an enormous number of different kinds of molecules, each of which generally performs a unique function. The entropy of a living thing is consequently much lower, atom for atom, than anything else in the world."

Smolin, Schrödinger, and many others see life as low entropy; as borrowing available free energy from the sun to create complex gradients that seemingly defy the second law of thermodynamics.

While this is a commonly accepted thermodynamic description of life, there are two separate arguments claiming that life actually creates more entropy (causes more disorder) than non-life. After everything we've covered in this book, this claim shouldn't seem at all intuitive. How could life, which creates complex gradients from disorder, create more disorder than non-living systems?

The first argument that life creates more entropy than non-life can be distilled down to the following; *Biological life dissipates more energy as heat than non-life.* To understand this statement better, let's briefly analyze one of the first and most widely cited papers which discusses the topic of life and the rate of entropy production. This paper, published in 1987 by Ulanowicz and Hannon (*Life and the Production of Entropy*), examined the question "Does biological life increase entropy faster than non-living matter?" The paper starts with the hypothesis that biotic (living) matter causes entropy to increase faster than abiotic (non-living) matter. At the beginning of the paper, the authors point out that this is a purely speculative paper and no experiments or quantitative analysis was done.

In their main argument, the researchers compare the entropy increase of a forest vs. a desert. The researchers concluded that the forest (with more biotic matter) caused entropy to increase faster than the desert (with less biotic matter). The authors of the paper gave two reasons for this: First, that biological life creates more heat than abiotic matter. Think of your own body for a moment. Touch your forehead or your chest. You radiate heat. All biological life radiates heat as a byproduct of our metabolism. You may not feel this same heat on a tree, but it's there. Just to a lesser extent than in warm-blooded mammals. Increased heat is linked to increased entropy production (think heat death of the universe). All of the equations for entropy show that as heat increases, entropy also increases. The second reason they gave in the forest vs. desert example is that life absorbs more photons than non-life. Rock and ice reflect more photons than does a canopied forest. Think of a mirror. That mirror absorbs very few photons, and instead reflects most of the photons that hit it. Rock and ice act more like a mirror in this way – reflecting photons instead of absorbing them. Life on the other hand (especially plant life) is very good at absorbing photons. The color and structure of plants make them greedy photon hogs – reflecting very few photons compared to a rock. The authors of the paper say this is significant because once that photon is absorbed and dissipated as heat, entropy increases. After a lifeform absorbs a photon, it degrades the photon's energy into a form that's no longer usable to do work. This absorption of photons and emission of heat is what researchers are referring to when they say biological life dissipates more energy as heat than non-life.

Another prominent argument for life increasing entropy faster than non-life comes from Eric Schneider who published an entire book in 2005 on this topic called *Into the Cool: Energy Flow, Thermodynamics, and Life*. In his book, Schneider argues that the function of biological life is to break down gradients. By breaking down gradients (free energy), life causes entropy to increase faster than it would in the absence of life. The gradient Schneider references is the thermal gradient between the surface of the Earth and outer space. Schneider proposes that life makes the surface of the Earth cooler and thus reduces the thermal gradient between cold space and the earth's hot surface warmed by the sun. The following are two quotes from Schneider's book *Into the Cool*:

"Life reduces the solar, electromagnetic gradient between the extremely hot (5,800 K) sun and the extremely cold outer space (only 2.7 K above absolute zero): it does so by erecting a planetary complex system and dissipating entropy, mostly at heat, into space."

"Ecosystems display a direction, an increase in gradient reduction over time. The more mature an ecosystem, the more solar energy it degrades...ecological richness correlates with temperature gradient reduction [between Earth's surface and outer space]."

There are other papers and publications out there talking about thermodynamics and life, but these papers mostly repeat some version of the two arguments presented by Schneider and

Ulanowicz. As you can see from reading this section, claims about entropy and biology range from Schrödinger to Schneider. Schrödinger and others claim that life is low entropy and creates ordered gradients out of disorder. However, the Schneider camp claim that life is actually a master gradient destroyer and makes entropy increase faster than non-life. Which way of looking at life and entropy is correct? In the next section, we'll take a critical look at these two arguments in an attempt to reconcile these disparate claims.

A Critical Review of Past Research

Let's first take a look at the argument that biological life causes entropy to increase faster than non-life because it dissipates more energy as heat. The main thing wrong with this argument is that it completely overlooks something else life does that has a lot of importance to thermodynamics and energy flow. This dissipative argument looks at only the beginning and the very end of the process of energy flow and life. The paradigm of the dissipative argument sees a photon entering a system and then sees heat leaving a system, but it ignores everything that happens in between. Yes, I agree that life dissipates more energy as heat than non-life, but I disagree that this causes entropy to increase faster. Instead of looking at biological life in this paradigm of "free energy dissipation", we should instead look at life as a system built for "free energy storage" (see figure 3.3).

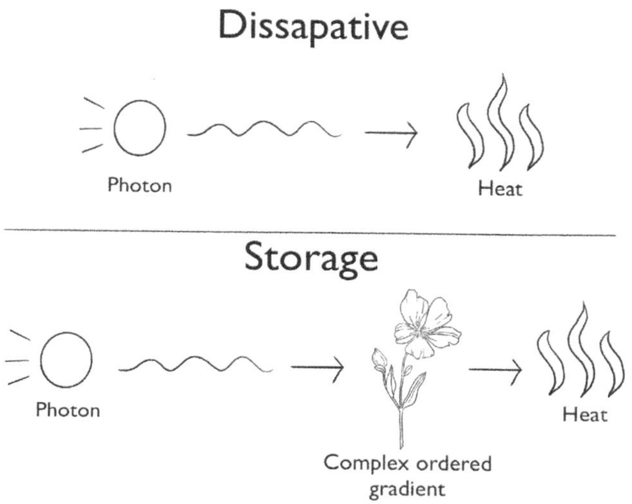

Dissapative

Photon   Heat

Storage

Photon

Complex ordered
gradient

Heat

Figure 3.3 Top: The dissipative paradigm sees only the inputs and outputs of the energetics of life. This paradigm has a blind spot. The storage paradigm is a more complete and accurate way of viewing the effect biological life has on the entropy of a system. Life does dissipate some energy as heat, but it does so as a tradeoff of storing free energy in the form of complex ordered gradients.

Life isn't just dissipating photons as heat; life is storing free energy from our sun in form of complex ordered gradients that just happen to give off a little heat as an engineering trade-off. The storage-based paradigm helps us see what biological life is really doing. Life is transforming and storing available free energy in the form of complex self-reproducing physical matter. Biological life isn't just degrading free energy, it's transforming it into a different state so that it can be used later. The more rich and dense an ecosystem, the more free energy is being stored in the form of biological life. What past researchers have glossed over is that biological life itself is a complex gradient of matter—and yes, to create life took an input of free energy (a gradient that was destroyed), but life captured part of this gradient before it's fully degraded. Life doesn't abhor a gradient as Schneider's book or Ulanowicz's paper suggests. *Life is a gradient.*

This book isn't written for a technical audience, but some of you may be interested in the math that backs up the storage-based paradigm of life and free energy. If you're interested in a more mathematical explanation for why energy storage is more important thermodynamically than heat dissipation, you can reference the appendix at the back of this book.

Moving on to discuss the second claim from Schneider that life causes entropy to increase faster than non-life because it degrades the thermal gradient between the hot surface of our planet and the cool void of outer space. The first thing wrong with this argument is that the temperature gradient chosen is somewhat arbitrary. There's a temperature gradient on both sides of the surface of the Earth, one below and one above. *Into the Cool* addresses the gradient between the surface of Earth to outer space, but what about the temperature gradient between Earth's core and Earth's surface? Earth's core is very hot (up to 11,000 F). If life is cooling the surface of Earth as Schneider's research suggests, then it's actually increasing the gradient between a cooled surface and a hot interior. Maybe life is working to preserve the temperature gradient between a hot core and a cool surface. Merely by looking at a different temperature gradient, the argument that life is reducing a temperature gradient is invalidated.

There's another big problem with Schneider's argument; there's not sufficient evidence to say that life is actually cooling the surface of the planet at all. Schneider cites ecosystems like rainforests as having a cooler surface temperature than deserts. However, the empirical data cited in his papers and book 1) doesn't measure temperature and 2) doesn't measure the surface of the Earth. Instead of measuring temperature, outgoing longwave radiation (OLR) is measured via a satellite. This satellite measurement is looking at the amount of light energy from the sun that was absorbed by our planet vs. what's reflected. Reflected light is not an acceptable analog for temperature, and shouldn't be used to speak to surface temperature. The surface of the Earth wasn't measured in this data either. The satellites collecting this data scanned whatever object they came into contact with first as they looked down on Earth. For measurements taken over the rainforest, tree canopies often weren't what was measured, cloud cover is what was measured. Because of evaporative cooling, clouds (and any wet surface) are cooler than a dry rock absorbing and reflecting light. The Earth doesn't need life to form clouds, but this is what has the biggest effect on the surface temperature of Earth as quantified by existing research.

The last issue with Schneider's argument we'll discuss is the problem of oceans. Two-thirds of our planet is covered in water. If biological life is a surface gradient reducer as proposed by Schneider, then why isn't the surface area of the ocean covered in biological structures that reduce this gradient? Schneider's research only looks at land masses and doesn't address oceans. It's hard to imagine how subsurface life in the oceans has any meaningful impact on surface temperature looking down from outer space. This issue isn't addressed by Schneider or other researchers publishing in this area.

Not only is the existing research far from convincing on the topic of biotic entropy production, but I also don't think researchers have asked the right question yet. Existing research has addressed the question *"Does biological life create more entropy than non-life?"*. A different and more relevant question to ask is *"Does a system with biological life reach thermal equilibrium faster or slower than a system with no biological life?"* This is a novel question that hasn't been asked or properly addressed before. This new question is the topic of the next section.

Life slows the increase of entropy in the universe

As we've already discussed, life is no paradox. Two sacrifices must be made to the entropy gods for life to exist. The first is that life is hot and entropy increases as heat increases. Our metabolism releases chaos in the form of heat out into the environment. The second sacrifice occurs in our sun. Life subsists off of a free energy stipend granted by our sun. This free energy is only released from the sun at the expense of a much bigger entropic increase happening from the solar reaction.

It's clear that life isn't reversing the entropic increase in our universe, but maybe it's slowing entropy down on its relentless march toward maximal disorder. As previously mentioned, this book isn't written for a technical audience, so I'll discuss this topic using thought experiments that are easy to digest and understand. If you'd like a more mathematical explanation, the appendix at the end of this book provides these details. For those of you not fluent or interested in math, this topic can be still be discussed effectively with a few thought experiments. Let's start by thinking about two photons emitted from the sun in our solar system. The first photon is emitted from our sun. It travels through space until it reaches an asteroid in the Kuiper Belt. The photon hits the face of the rock and is absorbed[4]. Entropy increases. The end.

The second photon is absorbed by the chloroplast of a leaf on Earth. This photon is put to work via a photosynthetic reaction. The reaction ultimately results in stored energy from the sun in chemical bonds of molecules like glucose and adenosine-triphosphate (ATP). Other life can then use the free energy available in the bonds of these molecules to create more order and more life. An insect eats the leaf and uses the energy in these molecules to sustain its metabolism. A frog then eats the insect. Then the frog is eaten by a small mammal. A larger mammal eventually consumes the smaller one. As the photon's energy travels through the food web, the complexity it enables compounds and grows. The photon absorbed by the chloroplast of the leaf

---

[4] Not every photon that hits a rock in space is absorbed. Many photons that hit an asteroid would be reflected back out into space. However, this photon would bounce around from rock to rock until it's finally absorbed somewhere without ever contributing to the increase of ordered gradients in the universe. For the sake of keeping this thought experiment as simple as possible, the photon is absorbed by the rock.

contributed to an increase of complex gradients on our planet. These were identical photons, but the results are very different.

The following thought experiment helps us answer the question *"Does a system with biological life reach thermal equilibrium faster or slower than a system with no biological life?"* To illustrate this thought experiment, picture two identical planets existing in two identical, but separate solar systems. One of these planets looks just like Earth with land and oceans teeming with life. The other planet is identical, except this planet harbors no life. Consider two huge tanks dunked into the ocean on each planet and filled by random chance. The tank dunked into the ocean with no life contains water, air, and some lumps of sediment and organic matter. The second tank dunked on the Earth-like planet with life is also dipped into the ocean at random. This tank got pulled up and is full of life. There's a shark, a few small fish, some plant life, and lots of microbes. There's also water and air in this tank.

The aliens who are conducting this experiment timed this sample collection so that both tanks are pulled out of the oceans at exactly the same time. After being collected, These two tanks are put on a boat and transported to the mainland. The alien researchers put each tank into a dark basement below the surface of the planet where there is no sunlight. The tanks are being put in this room for 100 years and will not be disturbed at all during this time. In 100 years, the doors will be opened and the researchers will measure which tank is closer to thermodynamic equilibrium. In other words, which tank has more gradients left in it than the other?

What happens when the source of external free energy (the sun) is removed in this thought experiment? Even though the external source of free energy is gone, life can still live inside the basement tank for many years. The shark can still eat the smaller fish to sustain itself for a few weeks or even months. Then it can use the free energy stored in its body fat to live off of. Eventually, when the shark dies of starvation – life in the tank lives on. Bacteria and fungi would live for many more years breaking down and living off of the free energy stored in the shark's dead body. Even after the bacteria die, the bones of the fish and shark will be in the tank. These bones are highly durable and would last for decades or longer depending on the acidity of the water. Any shells or exoskeletons would also last a long time after all the life in the tank died. Figure 3.4 illustrates this.

The first life on Earth was likely a simple single-celled organism. The entire complex tree of life branched from this simpleton of an ancestor. The more complex the lifeform is, the more free energy is stored in its biological body. The more diverse an ecosystem is, the more free energy is stored in a square mile of land. This is what we see as evolution has unfolded. Researchers have documented this phenomenon and call it the "arrow of complexity". Starting with a single-celled organism, we ended up with massive dinosaurs, giant sloths, mammoths, elephants, and great apes. The longer evolution goes on, there seems to be no upper limit for how diverse an ecosystem can be. As new lifeforms get created, this opens up new niches for new life to fill *ad infinitum*. This cycle would proceed unchecked if it weren't for the natural disasters and external factors that cause mass extinctions.

Biological life is like a bank account of free energy for the universe. The fact that this bank account creates a little heat, is an inconvenient engineering trade-off and is discussed mathematically in the appendix. Unfortunately, it's the way free energy works. When you force matter together in statistically

Tanks at initial collection

Tank 1: Lumps of sediment and organic matter

Tank 2: Biological life

Tanks at 100 Years

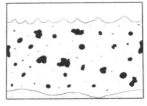

Tank 1: Closer to thermodynamic equilibrium With fewer gradients of physical matter

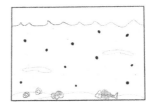

Tank 2: Highly ordered gradients of matter still in tank - shells and bones persist

Figure 3.4 Top shows Tank 1 and Tank 2 at Time zero right after they were pulled from the ocean. Tank 1 has big clumps of organic matter and sediment, but no life. Tank 2 is teeming with life. After 100 years in the basement, Tank 1 is much closer to thermodynamic equilibrium than Tank 2. Tank 2 still has a lot of ordered matter in the form of bones and shells.

unlikely configurations, it gets hot and angry about it. Heat production is like a financial advisor that takes a percentage of the wealth stored in the account. But over time, the balance in the account grows and it's worth it for the universe to keep its wealth under management.

...

In this chapter, I propose that biological life is a mechanism that captures and stores free energy to preserve gradients. This is a result of evolution by natural selection in a multiverse where there's selective pressure to slow the increase of entropy. These ideas might sound far-fetched when you first hear them, but I'm not the only one talking about how life is probably a functional adaptation in a multiverse. Dr. Michael E. Price published an entire book chapter on this topic in 2019 titled *Cosmological Natural Selection and the Function of Life*. In this chapter, Price points out that Darwinian selection would apply to a population of multiverses. He goes on to say:

"... *the first law of Darwinian adaptation [to consider is that] aspects of a phenotype that exhibit more improbable complexity are more likely to be adaptations. Because intelligent life exhibits higher improbable complexity (and therefore lower entropy) than black holes, it is more likely than black holes to be an adaptation for universe reproduction. From this perspective, biological evolution would represent a developmental subroutine of cosmological evolution, and the ultimate function of intelligent life would be to develop the knowledge and technology that would ultimately enable the universe to reproduce."*

While Price makes a similar point to mine, that complex life is probably a functional adaption in a multiverse, he doesn't propose any clear ideas on what exact function biological intelligent life evolved to perform in the multiverse to help it reproduce. If we live in an inflationary or black hole multiverse, slowing the increase of entropy would help a multiverse survive and reproduce. This is my proposal for the function of life in a multiverse.

So far we've looked at how biological life stores free energy in the form of complex gradients. In the thought experiment, we imagined two tanks of water – one with life and one without. After 100 years, the tank with life was further away from equilibrium, mostly owing to the hardy bones and shells left behind by life, but 100 years isn't a long time for a universe. In the next chapter, we'll discuss how the multiverse could select for organisms that can leave behind hardier gradients that last much longer than bones or shells. As we'll see next, intelligent conscious life can do something special that other life isn't adapted for.

Chapter Summary

- Biological life creates ordered gradients of physical matter from disorder, but does so at the expense of a larger entropy increase elsewhere in our universe.

- Life's ability to create gradients is likely the reason it evolved on our planet.

- Some researchers suggest that life degrades gradients, but their research is incomplete at best and misleading at worst.

- Both mathematical analysis and thought experiments show that biological life can slow a system down from reaching thermal equilibrium

- Biological life is a mechanism our universe evolved to slow the increase of entropy.

4

The Value of Human Consciousness

IF YOU HOP in your car in downtown Los Angeles and drive for three hours northeast you'll find yourself high up in the San Gabriel mountains – in a dark and secluded section of deep woods. A few mountain-man types live in that stretch of land, but that's not the main demographic. Instead of homesteaders and prospectors, this section of the San Gabriels has been claimed by Ph.D. astronomers. In 1907 construction of the Mount Wilson Observatory was completed. Researchers panned for shining nuggets of knowledge in the streams of stars for years after the facilities were built, but it wasn't until 1924 that someone struck cosmic gold with their telescope.

Erwin Hubble arrived at Mount Wilson in 1919, just after the observatory finished the construction of its state-of-the-art 100-inch telescope – the biggest one in the world at the time. Hubble spent his evenings sitting in a wooden Windsor back chair, looking deep into the glimmering eyes of the night sky, asking the cosmos to divulge her secrets to him. It took five years of courtship, but in 1924, the universe finally confided in Hubble. Within months of the discovery, the secret was out and published in the New York Times. *"Another Universe Seen By Astronomer | Dr. Hubble Describes Mass of Celestial Bodies 700,000 Light Years Away."*

At the time of this discovery, it was thought that the Milky Way Galaxy, the one we live in, was the only galaxy in the universe. At Mount Wilson, Hubble discovered the existence of the Andromeda galaxy. Or as he called it at the time, "an island universe" hence the title of the New York Times article. Other astronomers had seen the swirls of stars comprising the Andromeda galaxy, but wrote it off as a nearby nebula of stars within the Milky Way. It was Hubble that proved these stars were much too far away to be in our galaxy, and that a vast swath of space separated the Milky Way from Andromeda. Since Hubble discovered the Andromeda Galaxy, it's now estimated that there are at least two trillion galaxies in the universe. The deeper we look into the night sky, the more swirls of complex gradients we keep finding.

We've already talked at length about the second law of thermodynamics and how disorder in the universe is supposed to be increasing. It's not just biological life that should initially strike us going against the second law. The ordered gradients of physical matter in the night sky should also give us pause. If entropy is always increasing then how are there two trillion swirls of intricately ordered galaxies floating around in our universe? Are we sure the laws of thermodynamics got this entropy thing right?

The more we look, the more we should question this. We seem to live in a universe of gradients. The ordered structures of galaxies are composed of stars and planets- themselves forms of ordered gradients. Stars and planets form from disordered clouds of dust and gas. This should remind us of the discussion in chapter three about plants forming from disordered particles of atmospheric carbon dioxide and water. Cosmic structures and biological life aren't where this anomaly ends. Our planet is littered with the statistically unlikely human artifacts we've left around. The second law shouldn't be happy about the existence of skyscrapers, snow blowers, or wedding dresses. We live in a universe filled with complex gradients. How did this happen?

Just like with biological life, the ordered structures of our cosmos don't violate the second law of thermodynamics. The overall entropy is still increasing, but the universe has evolved ways to pool up gradients when excess free energy is available. Our sun isn't the only source of free energy out there. The big bang provided the initial supply of free energy that makes all the resulting order we see in the universe possible. This free energy from the big bang keeps flowing down its concentration gradient to create gradients throughout our universe. Free energy from the big bang is used to create the order we see in galaxies, stars, and planets. Even though this cosmic order is being created, in the overall system (the entire universe), entropy is still increasing (See Figure 4.1).

The singularity at the origin of our universe was much more ordered than the dispersed and spatially separated galaxies, stars, and planets in our universe today. The singularity was the mother

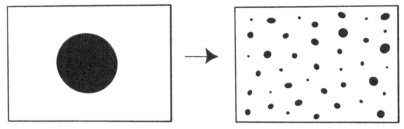

The very low entropy state of the singularity   The higher entropy state of our universe today

Figure 4.1: Left image shows the very low entropy state of the singularity before the big bang. The image on the right shows the matter and energy in the universe dispersing into galaxies and stars that are less ordered than the singularity. Even though there's order in the galaxies, planets, and stars, entropy in our universe is increasing as the number of microstates increase.

of all ordered gradients. Just like life borrowing free energy from the sun to create order, galaxies and stars borrowing free energy from the big bang to create order don't violate the second law. Entropy sill increases, but slower than it would have without the free energy being put to use.

Our sun and other stars aren't the only sources of free energy in the universe. The initial source of free energy in our universe that all others spawn from is the big bang. To illustrate this, picture our universe before the big bang like a reservoir being held behind a damn. As soon as the wall of the damn breaks, the water rushes out in every direction. It doesn't matter if we force some of the escaping water into pipes that capture hydropower from the flow.

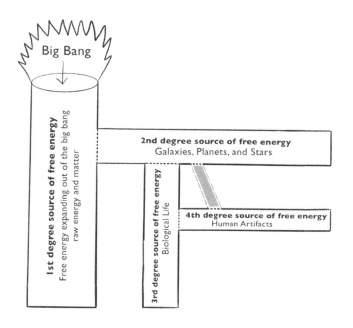

Figure 4.2 shows the cascading pipes of flowing free energy. The primary source of free energy in the universe comes from the explosion of matter and energy from the big bang. Some of this free energy is captured in galaxies, planets, and stars, a secondary source of free energy. Here on earth, some of the sun's free energy has been captured in biological life, a tertiary form of free energy. *Homo sapiens* have used the free energy captured in biological life (fossil fuels, food, and other organic materials) to create more gradients in the form of human artifacts, a quaternary form of free energy. In recent years, *Homo sapiens* have begun to capture free energy from our planet (tidal, wind, and geothermal) and our sun (solar energy) directly.

Overall the entropy of the system is still increasing as the water rushes out of the reservoir and disorder increases.

Visualize a big pipe put in place that captures as much of the flow as possible. The flow from the water main can be used to create gradients. Every time a new gradient is created, it's like a new pipe being fixed to the water main that diverts some of the flow. Since there is still water flowing in that new pipe, there's still gradient producing free energy in this side flow. A tertiary pipe can be fixed to the secondary pipe and so on down the concentration gradient of the water flow. The multiverse has evolved mechanisms that use the free energy from this water flow until every last drop has dried up (See Figure 4.2).

Following the thought experiment in chapter two, it makes sense that multiverse evolution would select for the most efficient mechanism to slow in the increase in entropy. This means putting all the free energy in the universe to work to create gradients and slow the increase in entropy (as Freeman Dyson pointed out in his 1971 publication about energy in the universe). We might be tempted after reading Chapter three to think that humans and other life on earth are rarities, but we're really just one small part of a much bigger picture.

Physicist Jeremy England has studied this phenomenon in great detail. England found that physical systems in out of equilibrium processes adapt their structures over time to become more efficient at capturing energy from the environment and dissipating that energy as heat. That's exactly what we see happening in Figure 4.2. Energy from the big bang is captured in the form of galaxies, planets, and stars. We can see the energy capture and heat dissipation especially well in stars (which give off a lot of heat). Biological life captures free energy from the sun and dissipates this energy as heat (touch your forehead if you don't believe me). Human and artificial intelligence artifacts do the same thing. One example is cities that capture energy inputs used to build them, and dissipate heat in the form of urban heat bubbles. Artificial Intelligence and computers do this, too. Energy is captured and used to order the atoms on a hard drive. The computer components and hard drive give off heat. The appearance of ordered gradients across our universe should not surprise us any more than a rock rolling down a hill or water flowing downstream. Free energy captured as ordered gradients is exactly what the universe is set up to do. A little heat dissipation is a side effect of this free energy capture and storage.

The Human Ability to Capture Free Energy

I grew up in the country in a house nestled on a four-acre plot of land. My childhood house sat on top of a hill that overlooked stretches of wooded land broken up by corn and soybean fields. Despite the ecological disturbance of agriculture, there was still a lot of wildlife in our area – and it always seemed to be trying to find its way into our house. There was a possum who made a temporary home under our back porch and the garter snakes that took up shop in our garden just outside the front door. Despite nature's persistence, my parents always found a way to force the wild animals out further again.

I remember one particularly intransigent squatter that didn't want to leave. Our front door had a light just outside and apparently, this light was the perfect habitat for a starling to make its nest. This nook was sheltered by an overhang, blocked from wind and rain, and high enough up that no predators could get to the nest.

The starling didn't seem to realize that it had neighbors. We couldn't walk out the front door without this starling initiating an airstrike. Even when we thought the coast was clear, we'd walk outside only for this starling to plunge out of a nearby bur oak and begin its intimidation campaign. When it finally achieved its goal of shooing us away, it would go back to the nest by our front door and puff up its chest in victory.

My parents finally found a time when the starling wasn't around. They went outside and used a broom to knock down the nest and sweep the remnants away. That very same day, the starling was back, building another nest. Within just a few days, a new nest was fully constructed and the starling was more emboldened than ever. This probably went on for at least two or three more cycles before the bird decided that the juice just wasn't worth the squeeze anymore.

I tell this story because, as a kid, I was scared of that bird. I used an alternate door for months- even after the avian aggressor had left. Fear wasn't all I felt though. I was also strangely impressed. As a child, I was awed that such a small thing could construct a home for itself so quickly, and all by itself. It would come back to a demolished home and have a new one built in days.

The starling building a nest for itself is an example of another animal building complex gradients. The starling nest was once a disordered pile of twigs and grasses. This bird used available free energy to create a complex gradient to live in. Birds can build nests. Bees can build beehives. Beavers build dams. Termites build earthen high-rises. We are not the only species that can use free energy to create ordered gradients of matter.

When hominids first started creating ordered arrangements of matter, our creations weren't much more impressive than the nest of the starling. *Homo erectus* made a stone hand ax, which wasn't much to marvel at, but we've since come a long way. We made it from hand axes to Honda Civics. How is it that humans can pull off these engineering concertos when the closest other social animals get are beehives and anthills?

The answer isn't just that we can cooperate and communicate better. Bees and ants have a system for communication and are experts at social cooperation. While our ability to cooperate plays a role here, it's not the whole story. The reason we can make such intricate gradients is because of our access to free energy.

The main difference between *Homo sapiens* and other social life forms is that *Homo sapiens* can access free energy outside of the niche in which we originally evolved. This is why we can build rocket ships that take us to the moon and why termites are stuck in the dirt.

Over time, humans evolved to access greater and greater stores of free energy available on our planet. We started off only having access to the free energy inside our own bodies, but we have far expanded on that as we evolved. *Homo sapiens* have since gone far beyond stone hand axes. Our evolutionary niche provided us free energy not only in the form of food we ate but also in the form of tribal cooperation to aid in individual survival. Aside from our food, evolution only endowed us with the free energy encased in about 150 individual humans. We used this free energy to create structures to live in, utensils for eating, and other tribal human artifacts.

It wasn't until about 250,000 years ago that we leveled up and gained access to the free energy encased in trees via burning them to cook our food. We used fire primarily to cook our food, which in turn grew our brains. The free energy available in trees was directly responsible for the cognitive revolution of our species. The cognitive revolution unlocked our ability to tell stories about money, nations, and religion. These stories gave us access to far more than the collective free energy available in a group of about 150 tribe members. So far, it seems the human story has no upper limit for how many humans it can bind together. The 1.5 billion inhabitants of China all combine their free energy based on the story of their nation that binds them together. The 2.1 billion adherents of Christianity all combine their collective free energy in the name of God. The story of money has enamored all 7.5 billion of us in the world today to do the bidding of the markets.

Money is probably the most successful story we humans have ever told. It's so successful, that you can almost equate a big pile of cash, to a big pile of available free energy. Money can be used to create ordered gradients and money can be used to slow the increase in entropy. Let's say you want to reduce the local entropy in your messy house. If you have money, you have a choice; you can either use the free energy available in your own body to clean your home or you can leverage the free energy in your bank account to hire out the job. Money is interchangeable with free energy that can be used to slow the increase of entropy. Money isn't just exchanged for services, it's often used to acquire goods. These goods are another analog for free energy. Much like a flower doesn't grow without an input of free energy from the sun, a Toyota Tacoma doesn't have a great statistical probability of being created from its constituent parts, without an input of free energy. Combined human free energy in the form of money is this input.

While money is the most universal way we humans trade our free energy, we have other stories we use that also result in a pool of available free energy. For example, religion compels us to cooperate and spend our free energy helping others independent of any monetary transaction. Religion may compel a group of people to go to another country affected by a natural disaster and spend their free energy helping to rebuild a devastated community. Many religions also encourage humans to create ordered gradients. This could be in the form of a cathedral, a mural, or religious iconography.

Telling stories is what enabled us to tap into the free energy potential of the entire human population, but that's not where we stopped. Beginning in the industrial revolution we found a new way to harness the free energy in trees. We began burning the biomass of trees, coal, and eventually, fossil fuels to power mechanical turbines. Today we are beginning to access free energy directly from the sun (solar energy), our atmosphere (wind energy), our oceans (tidal energy), and even in atoms (nuclear energy). Our consciousness is the mechanism that allows us to access free energy well beyond what was initially supplied to our hunter-gatherer ancestors in the form of food and tribal bonds.

This human ability to capture ever bigger caches of free energy is what makes us different from any other form of life on Earth. While bees are impressive social animals with methods of colony-wide communication, it's not nearly as impressive as what a human can do. Humans have figured out how to tap into stores of free energy on our planet and beyond – far exceeding the stores of free energy provided to us in our original hunter-gatherer niche. This is a truly impressive feat that no other organism on earth has figured out how to do. The human ability to capture and use free energy is what makes us truly unique.

Why We're Conscious

Very few evolutionary biologists think about human consciousness, but the ones that do are totally mystified by it. We know so little about human consciousness we don't even have a good working definition for it – let alone a good explanation of what evolutionary benefit it provides us. Neuroscientist Sam Harris defines human consciousness as *"An experiential internal qualitative dimension to any physical system."* Harris's definition can be broken down to mean consciousness is what it feels like to be you. This statement, while not untrue, only helps answer one of the three problems of consciousness.

Harris's definition answers the descriptive question of consciousness – or the question of *what* consciousness is and what its main features are. This definition, and most others, provide no answers to questions of *how* consciousness arose and *why* consciousness should exist. The question of why consciousness should exist is known as the functional question of consciousness. This is the one that a small minority of evolutionary biologists and phycologists puzzle at.

One of the current prevailing hypotheses is that consciousness is an evolutionary epiphenomenon. In other words, many experts think that our consciousness is just an accident of evolution and serves no real purpose for us. Zack Robinson, one of the leading researchers in this area, published a paper on this topic in 2015. Here is the abstract of Robinson's paper:

"Determining the biological function of phenomenal consciousness appears necessary to explain its origin: evolution by natural selection operates on organisms' traits based on the biological functions they fulfill. But identifying the function of phenomenal consciousness has proven difficult.... Perhaps phenomenal consciousness has no function of its own because it is either a by-product of other traits or a (functionless) accident. If so, then phenomenal consciousness has an evolutionary explanation even though it fulfills no biological function."

The conclusion of many who study this topic is that consciousness is probably a functionless accident that has no adaptive value. If you view evolution only through the lens of biology, then this is the logical, but unsettling conclusion. The current paradigm of biological evolution leads researchers to only ask the question *What is the adaptive value of consciousness for Homo sapiens?* The leading answer furnished so far is that consciousness must be a functionless accident of evolution because we don't need this trait to help us reproduce or pass on our genes.

Applying evolution by natural selection to the multiverse (also known as Universal Darwinism) provides a new answer to the functional question of consciousness. Suddenly, there's a clear and apparent reason why consciousness should evolve. The new evolutionary paradigm of the entropic philosophy leads to a new question; *what is the adaptive value of conscious beings for a universe?* In this paradigm, the adaptive value is not for us, *Homo sapiens*. The adaptive value of our consciousness is for the universe we live in.

To understand what the adaptive value of consciousness could be for a universe, follow me on another thought experiment. Consider a solar system with *a single star* and a *single planet*. Other than this star and planet, there is a great swath of cosmic dust, debris, and small asteroids orbiting the central star. On this lonely planet, biological life arises, and eventually a conscious race even more intelligent than humans evolve. This species is not yet capable of interstellar travel, but they can travel to small asteroids throughout their solar system.

Eventually, this species develops a technology that can harness energy from their star to concentrate the space dust and rocks into dense planets about the size of mars. There's enough raw material in this solar system to create fifteen more planets and even a few moons for each one. This species proceeds to colonize every planet and terraform each one to support more biological life. After creating fifteen planets, this species gets bored and decides to make space art instead of planets. They use their technology and energy from the sun to condense more of the space dust into massive installation art almost as big as the planets they made.

This goes on for a few million years until something very strange happens. All of sudden, the star at the center of the solar system just disappears. Poof. Gone. No more star. What's left is the 15 planets, the life on each planet, and all the art this species made. Compare this to an identical system with one star and one planet that never evolved life. The identical starting system that never evolved life has fewer gradients and is much closer to thermal equilibrium than the star system with life that went on to harness free energy from the sun to create ordered gradients from disordered space dust.

The existence of biological life and especially *conscious intelligent life* has the potential to drastically slow the increase of entropy in a system. Conscious agents have the potential to gain access to huge amounts of free energy that can be stored and used to slow the increase of entropy in the universe. Here's the entropic philosophy's answer to the functional question of consciousness:

Consciousness evolved to help living physical systems gain access to free energy in the universe outside of the original niche in which it evolved. Consciousness agents evolved in a multiverse as a mechanism to slow the increase of entropy. Physical systems that are not conscious cannot gain access to any free energy other than what is provided in the niche in which it evolved and have limited abilities to slow the increase of entropy.

The best we can tell, we personally gain very little from our consciousness. Flowers, turtles, and koalas can all pass on their genes just fine without being conscious. We don't need to be conscious to reproduce, but we do need to be conscious to access the free energy of a star in a neighboring galaxy. This is why a multiverse with selective pressure for longevity would evolve conscious agents who can harness free energy to slow the increase of entropy.

Consciousness and the Kardashev scale

I need to clarify that consciousness alone isn't what would be selected for. Natural selection by evolution would only favor conscious agents that used their access to free energy the right way. Free energy is a double-edged sword that cuts both ways. We can use free energy to create ornate gradients (good) or we can use free energy to blow up entire cities (bad). The only way consciousness is evolutionary advantageous is if the conscious system uses its free energy access to achieve the evolutionary goals of the universe. Consciousness not only gives us access to greater amounts of free energy; it also gives us a choice in how we use our powers. From a universal perspective, there are safety nets in place that ensure conscious systems that perform poorly don't have a meaningful impact. Natural selection has already taken care of this. Time is all that's required to find what the multiverse is looking for.

To better understand this, consider 100 conscious physical systems arising in our universe. For the sake of making this easy to visualize, let's say these physical systems look like humans and live on a planet similar to Earth. These planets have other non-conscious life living on them and a finite amount of resources and free energy available within their sphere. Now let's apply a standard distribution bell curve to these 100 conscious systems evaluating how efficient each system is at leveraging free energy to slow the increase of entropy. Based on the bell curve distribution, what we end up with is about 16 conscious systems that are really bad at slowing the increase of entropy, about 67 that are pretty average, 16 that are above average, and one conscious system that is an outlier at efficiently slowing the increase of entropy (see figure 4.3).

The systems that are below average at slowing the increase of entropy won't last long. By definition, these conscious systems will be forms of ordered physical gradients (like us). If they're exceptionally bad at slowing the increase of entropy, this will ensure their lifespan on the planet is brief. The blanket of disorder these systems create will envelop their planet and serve as their death shroud. They'll burn through all their available stores of free energy quickly; destroying the very gradients they need to sustain life on their planet. From a deep-time perspective, this rapid increase of entropy occurred over a cosmic blip of time and affected only a tiny volume of the universe. Given enough time, the planet will recolonize with new life and it will be as if it never happened. The worst case of consciousness gone awry has very little effect on the overall entropy of the universe.

The systems that are average at slowing the increase in entropy will likely survive for a relatively long time on their planet, but they will not be able to access free energy very far beyond their home

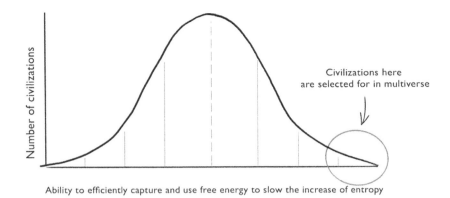

Figure 4.3. Take 100 conscious civilizations arising in a universe and apply a normal distribution bell curve. What this normal distribution tells us is that some civilizations will be very bad at using free energy to slow the increase of entropy, most will be average, and some will be very adept at using their free energy access to slow the increase of entropy.

planet. Since they're only able to capture the free energy on their planet, they are not able to colonize other parts of their solar system or other local galaxies. The effect is a small local increase of order gradients on this planet, but this too has a small overall impact on the rate of entropic increase in the entire universe.

The systems that are above average at utilizing their available free energy to slow the increase of entropy will have access to free energy well beyond that of their planet. This system will have harnessed the free energy on their planet, their sun, and maybe even parts of entire galaxies. These systems, by colonizing and building throughout their solar system and local galaxies, have spread ordered gradients throughout a much larger chunk of the universe. The overall impact on the rate of entropic increase is markedly lower in this corner of the universe's cosmic neighborhood.

Now, let's consider the single outlier system out of the initial 100. This conscious system is extraordinarily efficient at spreading ordered gradients throughout the universe that slow the increase of entropy. This system left its home planet long ago and colonized its entire solar system, local galaxy, and has now spread throughout the entire universe. The system can leverage the free energy available anywhere in its home universe. This conscious outlier has a massive impact on the universe's rate of entropic increase. *This outlier is what natural selection in the multiverse is after.*

In 1964, astronomer Nikolai Kardashev came up with a scale for measuring a civilization's level of technological advancement based on the amount of free energy they're able to harness. According to the Kardashev scale, a Type I civilization can utilize the free energy available on their planet. A Type II civilization can use all the free energy available in its solar system. A Type III civilization can leverage all free energy available in its home galaxy (see figure 4.4). How far we get on the Kardashev scale depends not only on our technological ability but on how we use the free energy we are able to tap into.

There's no real reason we couldn't someday become a type III civilization. Admittedly, our technology lags behind our imagination, but technological abilities might someday catch up. We've already conceptualized ways to capture the free energy from stars in a maximally efficient way using Dyson Spheres or Dyson Swarms. A Dyson Sphere encapsulates a star like a pebble inside a

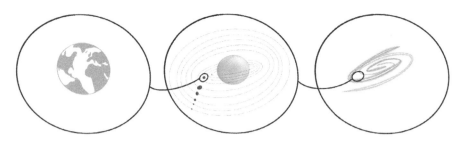

Type I: Planet   Type II: Solar System   Type III: Galaxy

Figure 4.4. A type I civilization has access to all the free energy on its planet. A type II civilization has access to all the free energy in its solar system. A type III civilization has access to all the free energy in its galaxy. Not pictured, a type IV civilization would have access to all the free energy in its universe.

locket. The inside of the locket captures all the free energy potential of the star and converts it into a form humans can use. Von Neumann probes have also been conceptualized. These probes would be fully autonomous and self-replicating. If you launch one into space, it would act as an invasive weed- spreading and growing everywhere. The probes could be programmed with some specific purpose in mind- and could work towards achieving some goal for humanity.

Are humans the best suited conscious agents on our planet to claim such a cosmic endowment of free energy? Weak artificial intelligence (AI) is beginning to write prose, make images, and build virtual words – forms of ordered gradients stored on hard drives and servers. A strong AI could do much more than this if it ever arose. Imagine a network of super-intelligent computers that run off of solar power. This network of supercomputers would be exponentially more efficient than *Homo sapiens* at utilizing their pool of collective free energy to create order. They wouldn't face the same gambit of the challenges and inefficiencies that we do like ego, emotions, mental and physical illness, and biological reproduction. They probably wouldn't kill off their entire population in an ego-driven nuclear holocaust. A superintelligence probably wouldn't myopically limit its ability to colonize space by trapping itself in an orbital shroud of space junk.

Our consciousness alone doesn't guarantee that we'll climb the Kardashev Scale. If we want to claim our cosmic endowment, we'll need to pass through the filters that select for conscious agents that use free energy to slow the increase of entropy in the universe.

...

Our universe should be teeming with other forms of life, and we should already know about it. This is the Fermi Paradox. The paradox comes from the fact that there is an extremely high probability of other intelligent life forms arising in the milky way, but we have absolutely no evidence that such lifeforms actually exist. There are billions of stars in the milky way similar to our sun and many of these stars contain Earth-like planets. If even a small fraction of those planets evolved life, and if a small fraction of those life forms gained the ability to travel space, then we should definitely be seeing some aliens. The Drake equation puts this estimate into a mathematical format. Frank Drake, the physicist who made the equation estimates that there should be anywhere from 1,000 to 100,000,000 planets harboring intelligent civilizations in the Milky Way galaxy. So where is everyone?

A proposed solution to the Fermi Paradox is that there are a series of great filters that life forms pass through as they develop. Some forms of life make it through these filters, but others don't. No one knows for sure what these filters could be, but we can start to see some issues on the horizon that could filter humanity out of being a type III civilization. Climate change, nuclear war, and our space junk problem could all hinder our ability to colonize the cosmos. Just because we're conscious doesn't mean we'll inherit our cosmic endowment of free energy. To realize our potential, we must make the right entropic choices.

The Entropic Choice

We as conscious beings have a choice laid out before us. On one hand, we can choose to use our free energy to slow the increase of entropy by spreading ordered gradients around our universe. Our other choice is to use our free energy to destroy existing gradients on this planet – including, potentially, ourselves. Acknowledging this choice means acknowledging our responsibilities with how we use the free energy we're gaining access to. Now that we understand the adaptive value of consciousness and our choice as conscious systems, we can no longer escape the mirror held up to our collective actions and decisions. When we look into this mirror, we should feel a mix of pride and shame about the reflection we see.

Let's first admire our positive attributes reflected in the mirror. When we look around our world today, there's no doubt that we've used at least some of our available free energy to create complex gradients. Looking first at digital gradients, by 2016 humans have created 16.1 zettabytes[5] of data (1 zettabyte is 1×10^{21} bytes). By 2025 it's projected that our datasphere will grow to include 163 ZB of information. 90% of the digital data that exists today has been created in the last two years alone. The pace at which we generate digital order is growing exponentially.

Digital gradients are relatively new on the scene compared to the gradients making up physical objects. We've been making buildings, clothing, and cars for much longer than we've been making cat GIFs. As of 2012, the United States alone has 5.6 million commercial (non-residential) buildings that together encompass 87 billion square feet. Updated census data around the world vary, but as of 2005[6], there were a reported 1.6 billion houses in the world. At least 80 billion garments of clothing are produced every year around the world and today there are over 1.3 billion motor vehicles on the road. I could keep listing these huge numbers, but you get it – we generate a lot of ordered gradients.

---

[5] For reference, a zettabyte is 1×10^{21} bytes. A Gigabyte is 1×10^{9} bytes. Apple's MacBook Pro 13 model has three options for hard drive size: 128GB, 256GB, and 512GB. Assuming you go with the middle storage option of 256GB; a single zettabyte is like giving 4 billion people, over half the world's entire population, a MacBook Pro 13 and having them completely fill it with data.

[6] This is the median census date of all the countries reporting the number of households in their nation. The actual census dates range from 2000 to 2019.

Maybe the most impressive growth of all is the physical order composed in the collective biomass of *Homo sapiens*. We are highly ordered gradients of flesh – and there are a lot more of us today than there were 12,000 years ago. In 10,000 BC an estimated two million humans populated our planet. Today, there are *five times* as many robots on earth as there were humans only 10,000 years ago! An estimated 7.5 billion people inhabit the globe as of the writing of this book. If we look at our global population as physical matter – we grew the amount of human biomass on our planet by 514 million tons[7] in the last 12,000 years. *That difference in human biomass is roughly equivalent to all the trees in Yellowstone, Rocky Mountain, Yosemite, Olympic, Smokey Mountain, and Glacier National Park[8]*. Let that human meat tree visual sink in for a moment. As our population grows, we're finding that we have more of an impact on our planet than previously thought.

Unfortunately, we humans don't just create gradients; we destroy them too. This has been going on for longer than most people give us credit. There's good evidence that hominids, including *Homo sapiens*, are responsible for the extinction of most of the world's megafauna. I'm not just talking about the wooly mammoth. The hominid slaughter story starts around 125,000 years ago and it repeated itself many times throughout history. Whenever a human showed up on a new continent, very shortly after our arrival the majority of that contentment's mammalian

---

[7] Assuming the average weight of a human is 137 lbs.

[8] Assuming the average acre of forest has 94 tons of tree biomass

megafauna would disappear. Examples of what we lost include a giant wombat from Australia called a diprotodon, which was the largest marsupial to ever live, at roughly the size of a hippopotamus. In South America, we lost the megatherium, a giant ground sloth about the size of a modern-day elephant. It's hard to say exactly how many species have now died off as a direct result of human activity. What we can speak to is the rate at which species are dying. In our current mass extinction event, species are dying off at 100 to 1,000 times the normal rate and we're responsible.

Humans impact the planet in many ways, but agriculture is one the biggest drivers changing the surface of our planet. Agricultural land use likely accounts for 70% of terrestrial biodiversity loss. Look no further than the Gulf of Mexico to see this in action. Pollution from Midwest agricultural run-off traveled down the Mississippi River and into the Gulf of Mexico creating a "dead-zone" in the ocean bigger than 6,500 square miles. This dead zone, where almost no oceanic life can subsist, is nearly the size of New Jersey. Agriculture is also a leading cause of deforestation. Even though the pace of deforestation is slowing, we're still losing forested land at alarming rates and the biodiversity that once thrived in that forest. In just the last 25 years, even with forest management efforts, we still lost over 571,000 square miles of forested land- equivalent to the combined size of California, Oregon, Washington, Nevada, and Idaho. The worlds' population is slated to increase to almost 10 billion by 2050 – which would grow the demand for food dramatically. The effects of agriculture on biodiversity are far from slowing down.

We've also begun to neglect and destroy our own creations of ordered gradients. According to the US Environmental Protection Agency (EPA), the average American generates about six pounds of trash every day. Over the year, that's over 2,100 lbs. of trash- or about the weight of a Toyota Yaris. This figure doesn't even include industrial waste which we all individually contribute to by consuming the products of industry. Very little of this trash gets sent to a recycling plant, and even if it does make its way to a recycling facility, that doesn't mean it actually gets recycled. The EPA says about 8% of plastics produced around the world get recycled and reused. Some of our trash goes to landfills, some gets composted, some gets recycled, but a large amount ends up as litter and eventually pools up in our oceans. It's not just natural gradients that suffer, man and man-made gradients suffer, too. Every war, every detonation of a bomb, every murder, and every violent destructive act leads to the destruction of gradients.

...

Current estimates place humanity between 0.7-0.8 on the Kardashev scale. We have yet to harness the full free energy potential on our home planet. Will we become a type III civilization and claim our cosmic endowment, or will we fail around in the dirt for the rest of our existence? Our future and the choice we make are fully in our own hands.

Most of us realize that ecological destruction isn't good; that we shouldn't engage in nuclear war, that we should take aggressive action to slow or stop climate change, and that we need to stop polluting our planet. Most want to stop our collective ecological destruction and wanton wastefulness, but this is where the agreement ends. For example, even those who agree that we should stop climate change, can't agree about who needs to take action, what action needs to be taken, and ultimately – we don't agree on why we need to stop it at all. Many can't even agree if individual action needs to be taken at all. Some place the blame squarely on corporations and corrupt governments and deny any personal responsibility. These warriors will never win a single battle and certainly won't recruit many to their ranks as philosophical discord guts their organization from the inside. If we want to make progress on problems like climate change, ecological collapse, nuclear war, and become better stewards of our planet – we need real guiding principles that clearly outline what we should do and why.

Our current report card is decidedly mixed. We use a portion of our available free energy to create ordered gradients, but our creations have come at a cost. Together, humanity has a conscious choice to make about how we use our available free energy and what we make with it. It's up to us to decide if we want to earn our cosmic endowment or not, but we won't make it far on the path we're headed. If we want to pass through the entropic filter, then we need clear guidelines and imperatives that will help us make it through together. If we all work toward a common goal, with a shared set of morals and imperatives, I'm optimistic that humanity could achieve whatever we set our minds to.

Chapter Summary

- The universe evolved ways to store the free energy initially released from the big bang in the form of galaxies, stars/planets, biological life, and artifacts made by conscious agents.

- Humans are better at capturing and storing free energy than any other lifeform on earth.

- A proposed new answer to the functional question of consciousness is that consciousness evolved as a mechanism to gain access to free energy outside of the original niche in which the conscious agent evolved.

- Conscious agents that effectively use free energy to slow the increase of entropy would be selected for in a multiverse.

- Just because we're conscious doesn't mean we'll be effective at using free energy to slow the increase of entropy. We have a conscious choice to make.

Part II

The Moral Imperatives

5

The Moral Imperatives

I'M NOT THE only Entropian, but for years it seemed that I was very much alone. The thought experiment outlined in this book formed in 2016. These early ideas were inspired by one of my professors, my graduate studies, and the writings of Nick Lane and Caesar Hidalgo. While I initially had this intellectual map of accepted and well-charted ideas, my thoughts and reasoning have since veered off into uncharted territory. After weathering the cerebral storm that led me to these ideas, I'd found myself marooned on a philosophical desert island.

In the ensuing four years, it seemed that I was indeed alone on Isle de Entropy. There were a few times over the years that I heard the voice of another swept away in the coastal wind. I'd search for the source only to find that these voices were not on this island with me. It turned out the distant voices of John Scales Avery (*Information Theory and Evolution*) and Jeremy Rifkin (*Entropy: A New World View*) had been carried in the gusting breeze from the philosophical mainland. Even calls from Eric Schneider (*Into the Cool*) and Erwin Schrödinger (*What is Life?*) were faint and distant – They weren't on the island either. I found myself alone with nothing but a new philosophical theory to mull over in my solitude.

After all this time thinking I was alone, Imagine my sheer delight, when I finally stumbled upon a small settlement that first landed on this island over 60 years ago! The first real settler of Isle de Entropy was Robert Lindsay back in 1959. Lindsey, a physicist, dared to posit that science could inform philosophy; as bold a notion in the 1950s as it is today[9]. His publication *Entropy Consumption and Values in Physical Science* reasoned that the second law of thermodynamics not only could but should inform our ethics. The following is a selection from Lindsay's publication:

"While we do live we ought always to act in all things in such a way as to produce as much order in our environment as possible, in other words to maximize the consumption of entropy. This is the thermodynamic imperative, a normative principle which may serve as the basis for a persuasive ethic in the spirit of the Golden Rule and Kant's categorical imperative... The very existence of life itself is a challenge to the operation of the second law, and that the only way to

---

[9] David Hume for example would take issues with this. Hume says the way the world *is* shouldn't inform what we *ought* to do. But others think science can inform ethics such as Isaac Newton who said that science can more accurately be called "natural philosophy" and can inform our ethics. Stephen Hawking took this a step further saying that "Philosophy is dead" and we should now look to science to answer the most pressing philosophical questions.

make the most of life, to fulfill its purpose, if it has any, is to continue to
respond to the challenge by maximizing the consumption of entropy
in every possible way. Only in this way can we successfully express our
feeling that life has meaning in the face of the remorseless natural
increase in entropy of the universe."

You'll notice some dated language in this paper. Specifically the term "entropy consumption". Erwin Schrödinger's 1944 publication, *What is Life?* contained similar antiquated terms like "negative entropy". At the time, terminology had not yet been concisely nailed down to describe out of equilibrium physics like it is today. You can see what Lindsay meant by entropy consumption below:

"The living cell is enormously complex in terms of the constituent
molecules, but these molecules are models of orderly arrangement. Life,
then, may fairly be said to consume entropy, since, with the transition
from disorder to order, the entropy of the universe decreases."

In light of new advancements, Lindsay most certainly would have rephrased this. We now well know that entropy in the universe does not decrease, and any local decrease in entropy is coupled with an increase in the universe somewhere else. Such is the case with the ordered gradients of biological life on Earth existing at the expense of the sun's entropic increase. Today Lindsay might rephrase this to say "Life captures available free energy to create ordered gradients that slow the increase of entropy in the universe".

What was controversial, and still is, is what Lindsay says next. He then goes on to say that life does something very weird; it does the opposite of what the second law of thermodynamics says physical matter should do. Biological life creates ordered complex gradients out of disordered bits and pieces. At the time, we'd observed nothing else in the universe that did this. To Lindsay, this was the sole purpose of life. To honor all life, and to live the most moral life possible, humans have a moral responsibility to use available free energy to create ordered gradients. He called this a *Thermodynamic Imperative.*

Lindsay mentions normative principles and Immanuel Kant's categorical imperative, which he borrowed from to coin the term "Thermodynamic Imperative". The typical reader of this book probably doesn't have an extensive philosophical background, so it's worth breaking these things down and defining some of this language. As you'll see, there's a lot packed into these terms. Hang tight through the explanation. It all helps in the understanding of what both myself and Lindsay are driving at.

First, to understand normative ethics; ethics is a broad field of study in philosophy. It contains not just a branch of ethics called normative ethics, but also branches of meta-ethics, applied ethics, and descriptive ethics to name a few. Despite the many branches of ethics radiating out of academia, most of us live our day-to-day lives using none of these. The average human makes moral decisions based on our emotions, not dense academic tomes. Philosopher David Hume knew this back in 1739 when he published *A Treatise of Human Nature.* In this philosophical treatise, Hume decries that reason will only ever be the servant of our emotions. Hume tells us that the field of ethics consists solely of *post hoc* reasoning that we construct to validate the emotions and beliefs we already had. Our human emotions, limited sensory organs, and innate biases do make the field of ethics a tricky place for *Homo sapiens* to tread. However, the field of normative ethics is concerned with finding a transcendent moral truth despite our human limitations even if this truth doesn't jive well with our emotions and biases.

The entropic philosophy fits neatly on the branch of ethics called normative ethics (see figure 5.1). Within normative ethics, there are more branches and theories. A big split in normative ethics is between deontologists and consequentialists. Deontologists believe that the intent of our actions matters more than the actual outcome that results from these actions. Consequentialists, on the other hand, say intent doesn't matter at all; only the outcomes of actions matter. Of course, there's a lot of gray area in between, but this the core rift between these two ideologies.

To better understand the difference between deontologists and consequentialists, consider an example. Frank and Patty are teenagers who need to mow the lawn as one of their household chores. Frank has been putting off mowing the lawn up until the last minute. He caused his parents a great deal of grief with his procrastination, and eventually had to be bribed to get the job done, but not before cursing his parents and telling them how much he hates them. In a different household, Patty acts very differently. She's the daughter of a single mother who works two jobs to make ends meet for their household. Patty doesn't need to be asked twice to help out. She's so grateful for all her mother does for her, that she's happy to help out around the house any way she can. She jumps at this opportunity to help her mother, who she loves and admires deeply. In this example, both Patty and Frank end up mowing the lawn. Because the same outcome was achieved, consequentialists say that there is no moral difference between Patty and Frank's behavior. Deontologists say otherwise. A deontologist would say that Patty is much more moral than Frank because her intentions were more moral. To a deontologist, the fact that the outcome was the same doesn't matter.

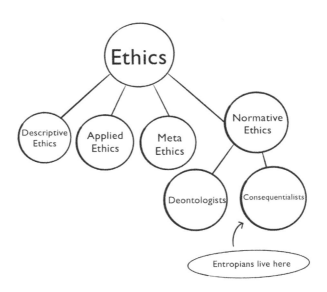

Figure 5.1: Different categories within the field of ethics. Normative ethics is a field of ethics split into two different camps – deontologists and consequentialists. The entropic philosophy falls in the field of normative ethics. The ideals of the entropic philosophy fall into the category of consequentialist normative ethics.

If you're an Entropian, then it follows that you're also a consequentialist. Based on the logic of the entropic philosophy it doesn't matter at all if we *intend* to slow the increase of entropy with the creation of ordered gradients. All that matters is that *we actually achieve the physical outcome* of slowing the increase of entropy in the universe.

Now that we understand what Lindsay meant by "normative principles", we can dive into Immanuel Kant's categorical imperatives that Lindsay also referenced. Kant was arguably the most influential philosopher of the enlightenment era. One of Kant's most revolutionary ideas can be described as an amendment to the golden rule. The golden rule says "Treat others how you would like to be treated." Kant reasoned that this wasn't a good rule to follow. This rule still leaves room for lying, cheating, violence, crime, and other immoral vagaries. Instead, Kant said the new rule should read "Act how you would want all other people in the world to act." Instead of an ideal that varies from individual to individual, this would serve more as a universal moral law that all people must follow. Kant called this idea for a universal moral law a *categorical imperative.*

To illustrate an example of a categorical imperative, we can look to Kant who believed there should be an absolute prohibition against lying. In other words, Kant believed it was a categorical imperative to tell the truth. He held that there was absolutely no situation that could ever arise that would make it ok to lie. Kant would say that if a known murderer showed up at your door asking where your spouse is, you shouldn't lie to the murderer. Kant believed we should tell the truth no matter what the circumstances are. A true categorical imperative has no gray area.

This is what Lindsay meant when he said that it's a thermodynamic imperative to *"act in all things in such a way as to produce as much order in our environment as possible."* Lindsay and I would like all people to act in this way – to live their lives in such a way as to use available free energy to slow the increase of entropy in our universe. Kant calls this a categorical imperative and Lindsay calls it a thermodynamic imperative. I think both terms are overly technical and instead call the ethics of the entropic philosophy the *moral imperatives*. Philosophy and physics are complicated enough without inventing more jargon to obscure new ideas even more. The next three chapters explain the three moral imperatives of the entropic philosophy. As we'll see next, there's more to being an Entropian than the single imperative Lindsay called for in 1959.

The math behind the morals

To better understand the moral imperatives, we need a better understanding of what it means to slow the increase of entropy. To achieve this, we need a better understanding of entropy. Equations provide the best understanding of this concept we have, so at this point, it becomes unavoidable to bring a little math into this book. I realize that many readers may be non-technical and will want to skip this part but hang with me through this section. I've taken the time to break down every equation, define every term, and make the math behind the morals as accessible as possible.

The thought experiment in Chapter 2 revealed a new insight. If we live in a multiverse, then natural selection by evolution would select for traits that slow the increase of entropy. So far, I've provided a non-mathematical definition for entropy as "*Increasing disorder; entropy destroys gradients.*" This definition isn't wrong, but a few equations can help us better understand what this means. Maybe the best definition for entropy was formulated almost 150 years ago by Ludwig Boltzmann. This statistical definition of entropy is captured in the equation below:

$S = K \log W$

Where:

- S= Entropy
- K= Boltzmann's Constant (Ideal gas constant/ Avogadro's number)
- Log= logarithm
- W= the number of microstates in a system

Before we start playing with this equation, let's get a better handle on what 'W' in this equation means. César Hidalgo provides a great metaphor explaining microstates in his book *Why Information Grows: The Evolution of Order, From Atoms to Economies*. In His example, Hidalgo asks his readers to visualize a half-full football stadium. First, we can visualize the lowest entropy seating configurations (microstates) of the stadium. The lowest entropy microstates would be where all the people are sitting packed together at either the lower half or upper half of the stadium (see figure 5.2). We can explain this as the lowest entropy state using our old definition of entropy, where low entropy states are rich in ordered gradients. In figure 5.2 we can see the gradient of filled seats neatly separated from all the empty seats. Using our new microstate definition of entropy, there are only two possible seating configurations in a half-full stadium, where all the people are sitting packed in together with no spaces in between. In this example, there are two possible microstates where this seating configuration is possible. In other words, W=2.

Now, what if we let the people in the stadium sit wherever they want and randomly disperse throughout the stadium? There are many different seating configurations possible that allow for a stadium to be half-full. In the stadium, each seat can be empty or taken such that a stadium with 100 seats has 4950 different ways each seat could be filled. So, in a randomly filled stadium of 100 seats, the number of possible microstates (W) is 4950. The randomly filled stadium has a much higher value for W and as a result, has a higher value of entropy than the neatly filled half-full stadium.

According to Boltzmann's definition of entropy, a 100 seat stadium with the first 50 seats filled and the next 50 seats empty is the microstate with the lowest possible entropy because it is the most statistically unlikely configuration of the system. It would be much more statistically likely to have 50 people scattered randomly through the stadium. A dense gradient of bodies in the first 50 seats is much more statistically unlikely than a random scattering of 50 people throughout the stadium. The main takeaway from

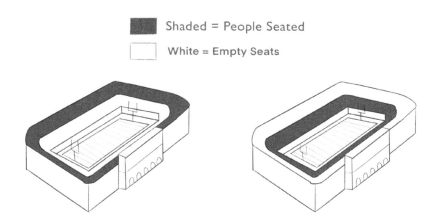

Figure 5.2: The lowest entropy seating configurations (microstates) of a half-full football stadium are where everyone is seated grouped together either in the lower half or upper of the stadium. In other words, the lowest entropy states are the ones with the most highly ordered gradients.

Boltzmann is that the lowest entropy microstates of a system are those with statistically unlikely gradients[10].

Now that we have a better understanding of both microstates and entropy, let's get back to Boltzmann's equation S=KlogW. Since K and log are constant terms that never change in this equation (like the speed of light is constant and unchanging) for

---

[10] As the stadium gets bigger, the entropy of the entire system increases. Shannon would say this is because the microstate of a stadium with 200 seats will take more bits of information to communicate than a microstate of a stadium with only 10 seats. Boltzmann would say the entropy for the bigger system is higher because there are more possible configurations. The more possible configurations there are, the higher the entropy of the system.

the sake of this proof they can be dropped from the equation. We now have:

$$S \propto W$$

This means that entropy is proportional to the number of microstates in a system. If the number of microstates increases, then entropy will increase. If the number of microstates decreases, then entropy will decrease.

Putting this in practical terms, think of our atmosphere as the stadium. Fossil fuels start off in a low entropy state because they represent an ordered arrangement of molecules that can encompass relatively few microstates. As we burn fossil fuels, we break the ordered molecules of carbon apart releasing individual carbon molecules in the form of CO_2. The individual CO_2 molecules now occupy an increased number of microstates given that there are more molecules (instead of one single long carbon molecule) and they are in a bigger stadium where it's easier to move around. In this example, the number of possible microstates increases, and this results in an increase in entropy.

Let's now take a look at the equation relating Gibbs Free Energy (G) to entropy (S):

$$\Delta G = \Delta H - T\Delta S$$

Where:

- ΔG= The change in Gibbs Free Energy
- ΔH= The change in enthalpy
- T= Temperature
- ΔS= The change in entropy

The Greek symbol Δ (pronounced delta) means "the change between the initial state and the ending state". For example, you could express the change in the outside temperature over the day as ΔT. If the temperature at the start of the day is 50 ° and at the end of the day, it's 60° then the change in temperature, or ΔT, is 10 °.

Since the Δ symbol is used so much in this equation, it's worth taking the time to understand. Why talk about the change in free energy instead of just giving a definite value? This is because total free energy is really hard to measure in large systems. Take the ocean for example. It's hard to measure down to the liter how much water is in the entire ocean and it's always in flux, but if you dump a two-liter of soda into the ocean then you know that the amount of liquid in the ocean due to that one reaction increased by two liters. Stated otherwise, that reaction has a change in volume, or ΔV, of two liters but this still tells you nothing about the total volume of liquid in the entire ocean. What this equation tells us is how much free energy was added or subtracted from a system (ΔG). This equation also tells us how much entropy changed due to this one reaction (ΔS).

For the sake of this analysis, I'm only interested in relating Entropy (S), to free energy (G), to the number of microstates in a system (W). To keep it simple, T and ΔH will be held constant and dropped from the equation[11]. So, if we drop T and ΔH from the equation what we now get is:

$$\Delta G \propto -\Delta S$$

Stated otherwise, the change in free energy is *inversely* proportional to the change in entropy. Based on what's discussed in this book, this statement should make intuitive sense. As entropy increases, the available amount of free energy decreases. Relating this idea to fossil fuels again—There is free energy stored in the carbon-to-carbon bonds of oil. This available free energy is released in the form of heat as we burn oil. After burning the oil, the free energy that existed in the molecular bonds of the oil molecule is lost forever as heat. As a result, the free energy of the system decreased and entropy increased. As we broke apart the bonds of the oil and chopped the molecule up into tiny pieces of CO_2, ordered gradients were destroyed. We can also understand this by using our non-mathematical definition of entropy where entropy= increasing disorder. This is still true, but we just have a better vocabulary to define what disorder is. Disorder is the

---

[11] This is fair because we're looking at how conscious life could affect the rate of entropic increase as a function of microstates and available free energy. There isn't much (we currently know about anyway) that a conscious life form could do to modulate temperate or enthalpy in these reactions.

increase in microstates. Disorder is also the decrease in the total available free energy of a system.

The final output relating entropy, free energy, and microstates using the above equations is:

$$S \propto W$$
$$\Delta G \propto -\Delta S$$
$$W \propto -\Delta G$$

Translated:

- Entropy increases with the number of microstates in a system
- Free energy decreases as entropy increases
- As the number of microstates increases, available free energy decreases

In order to minimize the increase of entropy, we need to slow the increase of total microstates in the system and maximize the available free energy. These equations are the basis for the moral imperatives discussed in detail in the following chapters.

The Moral Imperatives

Lindsay's imperative to *"act in all things in such a way as to produce as much order in our environment as possible."*, can be condensed to a single word: Create. This is the first moral imperative of the entropic philosophy and is the topic of the next chapter. But as we'll see, creating isn't the only moral imperative we need to follow if we wish to be the best Entropians possible; we also need to Steward and Conserve. These imperatives are based on the equations shown in the previous section. As a reminder, the math shows that to minimize the increase of entropy we need to slow the increase of total microstates in the system and maximize the available free energy. The acts of creating, stewarding, and conserving are the main activities that can help us achieve that goal.

After getting through the math, the moral imperatives that fall out are pretty simple and there are only three of them we'll discuss:

- Create ordered gradients with available free energy
- Be good stewards of both ordered gradients and free energy
- Use the least amount of free energy possible to achieve number 1 and 2 on this list (conserve)

These may seem simple but, there's quite a bit to unpack to help explain what each moral imperative means. Before we dive into the details of the moral imperatives, we first need a better understanding of who they apply to. While individual human beings are the basis for consciousness, we no longer act alone. We've created other conscious entities that now have access to free energy. The moral imperatives apply to us as individuals, but they also apply to the organizations and legal entities we create.

As we've already covered, humans have pooled our collective free energy by telling stories. We invented governments, corporations, and religions that now have access to the free energy encased in individual humans. The money these entities accumulate and spend represents the collective amount of human free energy they have access to. But these other conscious entities we created have begun to seek and use free energy beyond that in the human collective. Governments, corporations, and many religions now access free energy from fossil fuels, the sun, the wind, and even individual atoms. It may be strange to think of a government, corporation, or congregation as a conscious entity, but that's exactly what they are in the new paradigm of the entropic philosophy. If we want to claim our cosmic endowment and become a type III civilization, then no conscious entity is exempt from the moral imperatives laid out in this chapter.

Since no conscious entity is exempt, it's worth taking a moment to stress the individual responsibility we each have. Some recognize their responsibility but look no further than any internet forum where climate change is discussed to see the controversy. There's a rift separating those that believe action needs to be taken at an individual level and those that believe governments and corporations hold the key to change. Arguments rage on glowing midnight screens between two people who have taken up the same cause, but don't agree on a path forward. The good news is, everyone is right. There is an individual responsibility to follow the moral imperatives, but governments and corporations also play an immensely powerful role.

...

What we call our imperatives and how we define them aren't the only differences Lindsay and I have from one another. Lindsay's ideas and mine differ on quite a few important details. Lindsay didn't have the thought experiment about the multiverse and hence lacked a greater perspective on the role of entropy ethics beyond biological life. Without this idea, the only logical reason Lindsay could offer to follow his thermodynamic imperative is that this is what life does, so if we humans are the apex of life, we should do what life does, but do it the very best that we can. Lindsay also argued that we should create order as a way to show our reverence and respect for biological life. These are good reasons, but they don't seem to have been very convincing to a broader audience in the last 60 years.

The entropic philosophy gives a different set of reasons why we need to follow these moral imperatives. The reason why we need to create, steward, and conserve is because this is what biological life evolved to do. Conscious minds evolved in the multiverse to take these principles and colonize space with more ordered gradients. If we as conscious entities can't get a handle on these moral imperatives, then we don't have much hope at enduring long on this planet, let alone thriving outside of our solar system. What the entropic philosophy tells us is that we don't have a choice but to do these things. If we don't, natural selection will prune our species away for one that is better suited to the task at hand. The reason why we must act on the moral imperatives of the entropic philosophy is because it will ensure that our species not only survive long-term here on Earth but also thrives throughout the cosmos and can claim our cosmic endowment of free energy. These are the reasons offered by the entropic philosophy.

This idea of entropy informing our ethics first felt lonely, but as it turns out Lindsay and I aren't the only Entropians. A small but growing camp of philosophers, scientists, and engineers[12] have been stewing over the moral imperatives for many years now – With many getting closer and closer to the ideas laid out in the book. I hope you'll join us on Isle de Entropy, and eventually help spread it to the mainland. It's still lonely here, but the world needs more Entropians who will follow the moral imperatives laid out in the next chapters. As we've already covered– our global culture isn't exactly following these moral imperatives. We aren't efficiently using the free energy we've obtained with our conscious minds to slow the increase of entropy in our universe. We can do better.

In the next three chapters, I explain in detail how we can start using our cosmic gift of consciousness to start being better Entropians. If we follow these moral imperatives, we can ensure that humankind endures and thrives in the cosmos. We can make sure we end up on the winning side of evolution by natural selection in our universe.

---

[12] Luciano Floridi, Martin Flament Fultot, Xiaohong Wang, Ilya Prigogine, Mehrdad Massoudi, and George N. Saridis to name just a few.

Chapter Summary

- Robert Lindsay was the first to suggest that thermodynamics can inform our ethics and that we should create as much order as possible. Since Lindsay, many others have explored similar ideas.

- Using the equations for entropy and free energy, we can derive three moral imperatives of the entropic philosophy:
  - Create
  - Steward
  - Conserve

- Ideally, the moral imperatives apply to individuals as well as governments and corporations.

6

Create

"Our ability to create objects that are made primarily of information is what endows our species with fantastic capacities. Our ability to arrange atoms according to our imagination is what allowed a few of us to walk on the moon, and it is what allows many of us to enjoy long distance communication, food refrigeration, and long distance travel."

-Caesar Hidalgo, *Why Information Grows*

As I WAS filing for my first patent, it struck me how strange it was to claim ownership over an idea - a piece of my imagination. But the process of applying for a patent was far less captivating to me than the process of inventing itself. This was my first patent for my first invention. It was a microfluidic "lab on a chip" meant to process human cells for diagnostic purposes. I remember drawing out the designs on paper with branching microchannels of different depths and angles. Within three weeks of putting pen to paper, I was holding a 3D-printed prototype in my hands. I'll never forget the awe I felt as I picked up this crystal of my imagination for the first time. It made me feel like a demi-god; that I could imagine something and make it materialize in the real world.

The human ability to arrange physical atoms according to our imagination is what MIT professor Caesar Hidalgo calls crystalizing our imagination. I will shamelessly borrow Hidalgo's terminology, because it's poetic, and fitting. Engineers with 3D printers are far from the only crystallizers of imagination. A child drawing a T-rex with chalk on the sidewalk is crystalizing their imagination. A musician playing music for a live audience is crystallizing their imagination (albeit ephemerally in the vibrations of physical matter). A college student writing a term paper is crystalizing their imagination on the hard drive of their laptop.

Our consciousness gives rise to our imagination, and our imagination gives rise to crystals of ordered gradients. This power that we wield as imagination crystallizers *is* god-like. No other species on our planet has this power. We humans are dawning our wings and halos as we set a course to the heavens to colonize our solar system. We've cracked the genetic code of life and now have the tools required to fine-tune and manipulate biological life. The way we choose to wield our deific powers will determine what kind of gods we become. Will we be vengeful and destructive or benevolent and creative? Even gods need moral codes to guide their decisions.

The equations in the last section help define what a modern set of morals could look like. The entropic philosophy considers it a moral imperative to create ordered gradients from available free energy, but there are some nuances about creating to note:

- We should create things that will last a long time.
- We should create with diversity in mind.
- We should not create things that will quickly deplete stores of free energy or destroy gradients.
- Self-replicating, self-repairing, and self-colonizing gradients get priority over static creations.

The bullet points above contain most of the guidance we need to maximize our morality as creators, but each point on that list could use a bit more explanation. In the following section, we'll dive deeper into what it means to be a moral creator according to the entropic philosophy.

We should create ordered gradients that will last

To slow the increase of entropy most efficiently, creating ordered gradients that are stable over long periods of time would be selected for. Think about a multiverse that's approaching thermodynamic equilibrium (death). As we described in chapter 2, as long as there are gradients, entropy can still increase and work can still be done. By creating gradients that persist over long periods of time[13], we more effectively help slow the increase of entropy in the universe.

---

[13] Time isn't a man-made construct. Time is entropy. If we saw a video where the smoke of a campfire coalesced from the air and condense back into logs on the ground, we would say that the video was being played in reverse. Seeing entropy decrease as in this example of fire was the cue to us. Time travel into the past is impossible because it's impossible for entropy to decrease. The arrow of time heads into the future because the second law of thermodynamics says it must.

Typically, to create something stable and of high quality that will weather the relentless beating of entropy, more free energy will be required. The children's fable of the three little pigs illustrates this perfectly. The three pigs build three different houses out of three different materials all requiring different free energy inputs to make. The first pig made a house of straw which required the least free energy. The second pig made a house of sticks, which required slightly more free energy, and the third pig made a house of bricks, which required the most free energy to construct. The big bad wolf represents entropy in this fable. The straw and stick pigs spent their free energy playing instead of building a sturdier house. Both their shelters and those pigs succumbed to the wolfish fangs of entropy before the brick pig who spent its free energy laboring. The brick house was the only one that withstood the wolf's billows of entropic destruction.

The moral of the Three Little Pigs tells us that hard work and dedication pays off. The moral as written by the entropic philosophy would read: *Free energy, wisely spent, to create stable structures of ordered gradients will be more effective at slowing the increase of entropy in the universe.* We could sub that one into a children's story right?

We've all heard the aphorism "They just don't make 'em like they used to." It's true though. They really *don't* make 'em like they used to. We as humans used to make more brick houses, literally and figuratively. According to the entropic philosophy, if we're going to use precious free energy to make something, we should make something that lasts. We shouldn't make furniture meant to last 1 or 2 years in the dorms of college students. We should make furniture that's meant to stay in the family for generations. We shouldn't make clothing meant to be worn 2 or 3 times and then discarded. We should make clothing that will last years or decades. The same goes for consumer electronics, industrial buildings, housewares, automobiles, and yes- even houses. This concept of building stable gradients only becomes more important as we acquire access to more free energy in our solar system and beyond.

Creating Diversity

Creating and preserving diversity would be selected for in a multiverse population. To see why this would be so, think about the asteroid that hit the Earth 65 million years ago and killed the dinosaurs that ruled the land before their extinction. It wasn't just the dinosaurs that died out. Nearly 75% of all plants and animals expired as a result of this meteor strike. During the time of the dinosaurs, mammals were a footnote of biology. They were small, inconspicuous, and limited in numbers. The extinction of the dinosaurs created an open niche of available free energy which mammals adapted to fill.

What if there were only dinosaurs when the asteroid hit Earth 65 million years ago? All life on earth would have died, and the whole process of creating proton gradients in geothermal vents would have started over again from scratch. It makes sense that natural selection would create some safety nets to ensure that if there's a niche of free energy available, something will be there to utilize it. Diversity is this safety net.

While diversity is useful as a safety net, it does more for the universe than just this. Diversity also helps a universe more efficiently use available free energy to create ordered gradients. We can see this in traditional biological ecology with the concept of niches. An ecologist would define a niche as the role a species has in its environment. This includes how it eats, reproduces, finds shelter, and survives. What they could say instead is that *an ecological niche is any source of free energy that requires special adaptations to utilize*. Cyanobacteria, the first photosynthetic life on Earth, adapted to use free energy from the sun to grow itself. The Cyanobacteria themselves represented a new source of free energy that another organism could consume to create more ordered gradients. Zooplankton adapted to tap into this new niche of free energy from cyanobacteria consumption. In turn, more ocean life evolved that was able to utilize the free energy food sources. Diversity begets more diversity as new niches of free energy are created.

If Earth's history wasn't punctuated with catastrophic mass extinctions, we'd see an exponential increase in biodiversity. Even with these extinction events (like the KT extinction that killed the dinosaurs), what we see following the extinction is a radiation of new, diverse life adapted for recently vacated niches of free energy[14].

Biological diversity is often quantified by looking at the species richness of an area, but species richness is not where biodiversity ends. Even within a species, there is often a large amount of variation in traits. Consider us humans for example; within a population of humans, there's

diversity in height, hair color, weight, and many other physical traits. This diversity in traits is seen across the biosphere. If you take a population of *E. coli* bacterial cells and measure the output of metabolite X from each cell, there will most certainly be variation in metabolite production within that population of cells.

When I first started diving into concepts that would lead to the entropic philosophy, there was only one other idea that stuck in my mind as much as entropy. The concept of Gaussian curves, or normal distributions, clung in my mind and gnawed away at me just as entropy did. I found it so strange that we should see Gaussian curves everywhere in the universe. There's no physical law stating that data should be distributed around a mean in the predictable way we see with normal distributions. So why should we see it in almost any natural data set we acquire?

To conceptualize this point, let's go on a trip through our universe to collect data on a single metric: size. We start our cosmic field survey by first sampling the volume of different galaxies. We

[14] Romano, C., Goudemand, N., Vennemann, T. et al. Climatic and biotic upheavals following the end-Permian mass extinction. Nature Geosci 6, 57–60 (2013).

find galaxies of many shapes and many sizes. When we analyze the dataset, we find that the galaxies we sampled fit a normal distribution with most galaxies being roughly the same size, but some were much smaller or much bigger than average[15].

The next item on our survey list is planets. We hop from galaxy to galaxy collecting data on the diameter of all the different planets. When we plot the data on planets, a familiar curve appears showing that the size of the planets fits a normal distribution[16].

We round out our comic survey here on Earth to collect data on tree height. After all that intergalactic travel, we're a bit tired, so we decide to just collect data on the height of trees in Europe. We go from deciduous to evergreen to boreal and the resulting data is just what we expect at this point. The data shows a normal distribution of tree height in Europe[17]. We further segment that data to just look at the distribution of spruce height in Norway. The normal distribution persists. To finish up our survey, we collect data from a single spruce tree in Norway looking at the length of needles on the tree. No one on our field team is surprised

---

[15] Shiyin Shen, H., Mo, S., *et al.* The size distribution of galaxies in the Sloan Digital Sky Survey. Roy. Astron. Soc. (2003).

[16] Zeng, L., Stein, J., et al. Survival function analysis of planet size distribution with Gaia Data Release 2 updates. Monthly Notices of the Royal Astronomical Society, Volume 479, Issue 4, p.5567-5576 (2018).

[17] Vauhkonen, Jari. Estimating single-tree attributes by airborne laser scanning: methods based on computational geometry of the 3-D point data. Dissertationes Forestales. 104. (2010).

to see the data fits a normal bell-shaped curve. The data from our survey is shown in Figure 6.1.

The data collected on our field survey is imaginary but the ubiquity of Gaussian curves is not. Gaussian curves permeate any data set collected on any physical matter in our universe. Why should that be? In an introductory statistics course, students learn that most data take on a Gaussian distribution, but even the most advanced statistics course offers no answer for why we should see data distributed this way. The reason we see Gaussian distributions is because evolution by natural selection in a population of universes would be selecting for this. The spread of data in Gaussian curves ensures diversity of all physical matter in the universe. This diversity is selected for because it allows for efficient use of available free energy in different niches and it provides a safety net to ensure that if the environment changes, something will be adapted to fill the newly available niche of free energy.

The reach of Gaussian curves bends and warps our human creations. With few exceptions, we *Homo sapiens* already make a diverse variety of ordered physical gradients. Take for example computers sold in the year 2021. If you collect data on these computers regarding processing speed, memory, and screen size you will find data distributed in normal distributions. That's because these computers are needed for a diverse range of functions from gaming, to medical care, to writing college term papers.

The free market of our global economy is a powerful tool for diversity generation. When a free market is defined using the new language of the entropic philosophy, it makes sense why this would

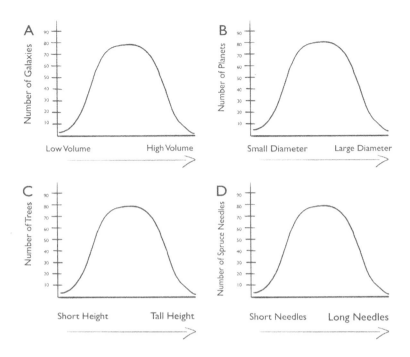

Figure 6.1: The imaginary data from our intergalactic field survey showing: A) The volume distribution of galaxies B) Distribution of planetary diameter C) Distribution of tree height in Europe D) Distribution of needle length on a single Norwegian spruce tree.

be so. The free market is driven entirely by human thoughts, feelings, and desires. We humans are bits of physical matter in our universe whose evolution was guided by thermodynamic constraints. Gaussian curves already permeate us, body and mind. This is why it makes sense that our needs, our thoughts, and our desires would be as diverse as we are. The free market caters to our diversity and thrives on it. As long as we embrace human diversity, the free market will continue to drive the diversity in our creations[18].

What we shouldn't make

As we've already discussed, a multiverse wouldn't select for anything that burns through free energy and quickly destroys gradients. The example given previously was a nuclear weapon that uses free energy to quickly lay waste to any physical gradient it encounters. Nuclear weapons aren't the only example of this entropic failure. Any weapon intended solely for warfare or violence falls in this category. This includes any type of bomb, missile, grenade, firearms intended for warfare, and biological, chemical, or digital weapons.

According to the entropic philosophy, we shouldn't make weapons (gradient destroyers) and we shouldn't engage in warfare (the act of destroying gradients). Warfare violates all three of the moral imperatives. To fight a war, a conscious entity must first make immoral creations meant to destroy gradients; then proceed to destroy gradients in the form of human life and human artifact gradients while wildlife suffers as an unintended casualty. All this while using up our limited supplies of life-sustaining free energy in the sole pursuit of destruction. Imagine an intergalactic type III civilization and the destruction they could leave on their warpath. Entire planets, solar systems, and maybe other forms of life could

---

[18] The ethics of free markets in capitalism are discussed more in Chapter 11.

be destroyed. The gradient destruction power of a type III civilization at war is nearly unlimited.

Weapons meant to wage wars aren't the only class of weapons we make. Lately, we've gotten very good at weaponizing pollutants against other life on our planet and ourselves. Let's take a cosmic perspective on pollution to better understand what pollution really is. Here on Earth, a pollutant is any physical matter that can harm or kill biological life. Pollution is a concept that is unique to planets that already harbor life or planets where life is intended to be created in the future.

To understand this statement better, follow me on a thought experiment set in the distant future. Imagine that *Homo sapiens* has colonized our solar system. We've been able to terraform not just Mars, but also Venus, and the moons of the gas giants. These planets and moons now teem with self-replicating biological life that originated on Earth. Try as they might, this technologically advanced civilization can't terraform Pluto to support biological life. However, there's still free energy available on the surface of Pluto from the sun that they wish to use to create ordered gradients. Instead of biological life, they build a series of solar-powered industrial plants on Pluto that capture material from small asteroids, space rocks, and ambient cosmic dust. These machines condense these space rocks into a cake of raw building material. This material is then mixed with synthetic polymers derived from biomass on the terraformed surface of Neptune's moon, Halimede. The polymer mix was transported to Pluto using solar-powered space vehicles. With a few chemical reactions of the space dust and the carbon-based synthetic polymers, they're able to create a material with very similar properties to polypropylene plastic. For reasons our simple and lowly evolved 21st-century minds can't understand, this advanced future race of humans has decided to shape this material on Pluto into plastic cutlery. Over the course of thousands of years, Pluto's surface becomes covered in a thick layer of plastic spoons, knives, forks, and even a few rare and elusive sporks.

Let's analyze what happened on Pluto. The increase of entropy was slowed by using available free energy from the sun to create ordered gradients in the form of plastic cutlery. Floating cosmic dust and ambient space rocks were compressed to create a statistically unlikely gradient of ordered physical matter. This was aided by growing biomass on Neptune's moon and transporting it using solar power. Solar power was used to process the space cake and the biomass derivative to create a plastic-like material. The result was the creation of ordered gradients from available free energy which slows the increase of entropy. While strange, this future human race still gets an approving nod from the entropic philosophy.

So what's wrong with single-use plastics on Earth? The problem is that the surface of the earth is already covered in statistically unlikely ordered gradients in the form of biological life. Biological life gets weighted as more valuable than single-use plastics for a couple of reasons: First, biological life is self-replicating meaning that it's statistically unlikely wonder will be more resilient to entropy than a piece of plastic. The second reason is that biological life is diverse. Every organism evolved over time to perfectly fit a specific niche of available free energy. This diversity also makes life more resilient, long-lived, and more efficient at storing available free energy than a plastic spoon.

Evolution wouldn't select for single-use plastics here on Earth in their current form. Evolution has created a carefully orchestrated dance of ecology with every available niche of free energy being filled. Single-use plastics are shutting down nature's carefully choreographed dance party. Here on Earth, single-use plastics are like a belligerent drunk who wandered on stage during a performance of La Bayadère, causing the music to stop and the magic of the dance to end.

By definition, single-use plastics are used once and then discarded. Once discarded, they either end up as litter, go to a landfill, or in rare cases actually get recycled. Landfills take away habitats for biological life to flourish, but they're the least of our worries. Many single-use plastics end up spread across the land as litter before eventually making it to the ocean. According to a 2015 study out of the University of California Santa Barbra, 8 million tons of plastic end up in the ocean every year. That's equivalent to dumping a garbage truckload every minute. A separate 2016 study from the Ellen MacArthur Foundation concluded that at this rate, by 2025 the ocean would contain 1 ton of plastic for every 3 tons of fish. Extrapolating this trend to 2050 means that this is the year where the ocean will contain more plastic than fish by weight. Plastics in the form of packaging account for the vast majority of this pollution.

The problem with all this plastic in the environment is that life didn't evolve to flourish in a plasticized niche. Wildlife is getting tangled up in plastic debris and ingesting it. A 2011 study estimated that in the North Pacific alone, fish ingest up to 24,000 tons of plastic each year[19]. This plastic bio-acclimates as smaller fish are eaten by bigger fish up the food chain. It's not just the fish eating it.

The actual number is sure to be higher. To date, there is little ongoing research outside of marine biology on the effects of plastics on wildlife. Without research, we should err on the side of caution and assume there are similar effects to terrestrial life that we have yet to document.

And then there are the effects of plastics on us humans. A 2011 overview of the public health impacts of plastics published in the Indian Journal of Occupational and Environmental Medicine finds that "Exposure to harmful chemicals during manufacturing, leaching in the stored food items while using plastic packages or chewing of plastic teethers and toys by children are linked with severe adverse health outcomes such as cancers, birth defects, impaired immunity, endocrine disruption, developmental and reproductive effects, etc."

At this point, we've pretty well established that plastics are harmful to life on earth during and after their use. The same is true for the front end of plastics as well. Fossil fuels are the feedstocks for almost all plastics. Polyethylene for example can be made from a feedstock of natural gas, oil, and even coal. Accessing deposits of fossil fuels buried deep underground often results in habitat

---

[19] Davidson, P., Asch, R. Plastic ingestion by mesopelagic fishes in the North Pacific Subtropical Gyre. Marine Ecology Progress Series, Volume 432, 173-180 (2011).

destruction and environmental damage. Such is the case with strip mining and mountaintop removal methods implemented for mining coal. Spills and accidents during natural gas and oil extraction aren't uncommon. In 2015 a pipeline used for fracking burst and released almost 3 million gallons of fracking brine into the environment. Then there's the grand poobah of fossil fuel induced environmental disasters – The 2010 BP oil spill which released nearly 1,000,000 gallons of crude oil into the pacific ocean. Plastics cost us on the front end of their production, too.

As we covered in the thought experiment at the beginning of this section, plastics aren't an entropic evil in and of themselves. It's all about context. However, in the current context, plastics should be shunned for their destructive effects on human and animal life on earth. Long term, the only way out of this plastic pickle we got ourselves into is to stop manufacturing and using plastics. Life didn't evolve to live in a plasticized niche. If we keep spreading plastic around the surface of the Earth, we shouldn't be surprised when the delicate waltz of nature stops, and even humans are asked to bow out of this biological dance.

While plastics illustrate a clear example of our immoral creations, they are far from the only thing we need to stop making. We need to stop creating any pollutant that threatens the vitality and diversity of biological life. This includes not only plastics but any form of pollution that kills life. If we create an object and in doing so life on Earth suffers, then we should view this no differently than the production of weapons. As far as life is concerned, plastic is a weapon and so are pollutants like lead, ozone, and chlorofluorocarbons.

...

Aristotle is quoted as saying "Nature abhors a vacuum". If Aristotle knew about concepts like out of equilibrium processes, entropy, and free energy, he may very well have rephrased this quip. Instead, he might have mused that *out of equilibrium processes with available free energy tend to create ordered gradients.* As conscious entities with access to stores of free energy, we have a moral obligation to create. Imagination and creativity are already a part of our species, but by following the guidelines laid out in this moral imperative, we can ensure that we fill the vacuum with things that help gradients persist in our universe.

We've talked at length in this chapter about creation, but this is only part of the story when it comes to slowing the increase of entropy. To be truly effective Entropians we also need to be good stewards. The next chapter will help us understand how stewarding ordered gradients can help slow the increase of entropy in our universe.

- The first moral imperative of the entropic philosophy is to create.

- Some creations are more "moral" than others.

- To most effectively slow the increase of entropy in our universe we should:
  - Create things that will last a long time.
  - Create diversity
  - Not create things that will quickly deplete stores of free energy or destroy gradients.

- Self-replicating, self-repairing, and self-colonizing gradients get priority over static creations.

7

Steward

"A thing is right when it tends to preserve the integrity, stability and beauty of the biotic community. It is wrong when it tends otherwise."

— Aldo Leopold, *A Sand County Almanac*

IN HIS 1949 BOOK *A Sand County Almanac*, Aldo Leopold makes an argument for a stewardship philosophy he coined The Land Ethic. In his book, Leopold touches on ideas similar to those expressed here. For example, he describes the land as an open circuit, with energy flowing in from the sun, then radiated through the food web in different ecological niches. Aldo Leopold was one of the first ecological ethicists to see that the land and the creatures that inhabit it have intrinsic value outside of servicing an economic purpose. He refers to this then polarizing idea as the *A-B cleavage* between two types of people who regarded the land as having value. Leopold describes these two groups in *A Sand County Almanac*:

"Group (A) regards the land as soil, and its function as commodity-production; another group (B) regards the land as biota, and its function as something broader. How much broader is admittedly in a state of doubt and confusion."

This last sentence of his description of Group B is where Leopold and I diverge. I too, fall in Leopold's Group B, but unlike Leopold, I'm able to articulate why biological life and natural land have value in the paradigm of the entropic philosophy. I don't want to deride Leopold's Land Ethic too much, because ultimately I think he landed on the right ethics. However, The Land Ethic fails to offer any reason *why* other life on earth ought to be treated as having intrinsic value. Leopold makes the argument that we should be better stewards of the land because it has intrinsic value, but he offers no logic or reasoning outside of emotion or intuition to back up this claim.

Aldo Leopold isn't the only environmental ethicist who failed to offer a reason why land and other life on earth should be protected. To date the reasons provided by other ethicists for stewarding our land and biota can be condensed down to the following three points:

1. Steward it because it has value to humans, economic or otherwise.
2. Steward it because land and life have rights similar to human rights.

3. Steward it because it has inherent value that we can all perceive.

Other than point number one, these philosophical reasons to steward make little logical sense. They're rooted in emotion and contain little logic or reasoning behind them. Aldo Leopold made a stewardship argument that falls under the second and third points above. These arguments have proved weak and ineffective at convincing us to take appropriate action. The moral ideal of the entropic philosophy doesn't discount any of these ideas, but a main difference is that the entropic philosophy is the only environmental philosophy that offers a reason *why* any of the points above are valid and require immediate action. The entropic philosophy imbues conservation ethics with logic and reasoning that were previously missing.

So-called Deep Ecology is another school of environmental ethics that invokes arguments two and three above but differs notably from Leopold's Land Ethic. Deep Ecology, first proposed in 1973 in an essay by Norwegian philosopher Arne Næss, has taken on a far more sinister bent than Næss originally intended. His philosophical essay was inspired by the iconic conservation text by Rachel Carson, *A Silent Spring*. The central idea is that the well-being of any part of an ecosystem depends on the overall well-being of the whole. This idea, like Leopold's, offers a philosophical basis for environmentalism. In his lifetime Næss supported nonviolent environmental activism, but others have since taken up his philosophy with a different spirit.

Many that support the Deep Ecology philosophy today use Næss's ideas to justify a rationale for upending technological progress. Modern supporters of Deep Ecology say that in order to preserve wilderness and biodiversity, human population control is needed and that this resulting smaller population of humans must live as simply as possible. These ideals were further fueled by Edward Abbey's 1975 novel, *The Monkey Wrench Gang*, which advocated for the destructive protest of environmentally damaging activities.

The philosophy of Næss, Carson, and Abbey eventually served as the nucleus for the formation of the Earth First! group in 1979. Since its inception in the '70s, sects of Earth First! have morphed into an eco-terrorism group known as the Earth Liberation Front and the Earth Liberation Army. These groups are responsible for acts of arson and violence all in the name of conservation and environmentalism.

The train wreck of the Deep Ecology movement culminated in the 1995 philosophical text by Theodore Kaczynski. Kaczynski is better known as the Unabomber and his 1995 publication is widely known as the Unabomber Manifesto. In his manifesto, the Unabomber provides a rationale for his 17-year stint of violence and murder. Kaczynski, citing inspiration from Earth First!, reasoned that human progress in the form of industrial technology is destroying our planet and destroying human happiness. He justified his bombings as a way to thwart human progress so that we can go back to a pre-industrial way of living.

The current environmental ethics paradigm abhors progress, technology, and rising human populations. Næss himself promoted the idea that the ideal population size of Earth should not surpass 100 million. While Næss did not directly rejoice when droughts and famine reduced local parts of the Earth's population, many supporters of Deep Ecology do. A great number of environmentalists are technophobes with genetic engineering being one of the most widely detested technological advancements. This lead both the Unabomber and the Earth Liberation Front to target genetic engineering laboratories for their acts of terrorism and violence.

The state of environmental ethics today is in shambles. Not only have the philosophies proposed in the last century been ineffective, leading to very little protection of biodiversity and wilderness, but they have also resulted in violence, destruction, and a camp of technological luddites who refuse to adopt or support technologies that could alleviate human suffering. To be an environmentalist in today's paradigm is often synonymous with being anti-technology and anti-progress.

The entropic philosophy doesn't negate the basic augments of traditional environmental ethics. The ethics provided in this book argue for fierce and strict stewardship of wilderness areas and biodiversity. Where the entropic philosophy diverges, is that it also argues for more than stewardship. It also argues for creation, progress, the alleviation of human suffering through technology, and space colonization – all in conjunction with a reverence and a responsibility to steward human life. The moral imperative of stewardship in the entropic philosophy provides a new paradigm for environmentalism; one that is compatible with technology, progress, and a growing human population[20].

What's more, traditional environmental ethics only provides stewardship guidelines for ordered gradients that take the form of biological life and land on earth. As we've learned from previous chapters, gradients of order abound in our universe and we have a moral obligation to steward all of it; not just the small subset we see right in front of us on our home planet.

If we aspire to colonize our solar system, galaxy, and potentially our entire universe, we need guidelines that ensure we steward all of nature's statistically unlikely wonder – not just that embodied in our pale blue dot.

Hierarchy of Free Energy Use

Before we dive into the specific instructions supplied by the entropic philosophy on how to be a good steward, we need to better understand some basic concepts around how we humans use our available free energy supply. As we'll discover in this section, stewarding and creating are a privilege that not all humans currently have the free energy resources to participate in.

---

[20] The entropic philosophy is compatible with a growing human population in the long term. However, in the short term, it would be ideal to slow population growth until processes and solutions are in place that help us efficiently steward life and land on earth. Taking a more long-term view, human population growth will be an inevitable and encouraged result of space colonization.

In 1943 Abraham Maslow published his new theory of human psychology in a paper called *"A Theory of Human Motivation"* (see Figure 7.1). Maslow theorized that human needs and desires could be placed in a hierarchy and that each human will seek to meet our most basic needs before climbing up the pyramid to more advanced desires. For example, an individual that's on the verge of dying of thirst isn't concerned with cultivating new friendships or painting a new masterpiece. A person needs to have their basic physiological needs met before moving up a rung on the hierarchy. After basic needs are met, then there's a motivation to seek safety and security. After security is attained, desire arises to find love and social acceptance. The final rung at the top of the ladder is self-actualization, which includes the motivation to pursue goals and develop new talents.

With some intellectual acrobatics, we can view Maslow's Hierarchy of Needs from a new angle that describes human free energy consumption behavior. Life, human or not, is at constant war with entropy. Without free energy inputs to sustain our physiology, we'll succumb to the unyielding abrasion of the second law of thermodynamics. For this reason, humans must first ensure that our physiological needs are met before using available free energy in any other way. After ensuring our physical metabolic needs are met, we can then use available left over free energy to build up safety and security. Once we feel secure, we can use our consciousness to start seeking out more access to new pools of free energy. We can do this through relationships with others to help us access the free energy in the physiology of the tribe. Evolutionarily there's a strong incentive to lean on parents,

Figure 7.1. Maslow's Hierarchy of Needs is often shaped like a pyramid to represent that the needs at the bottom are the foundation on which all further desires and motivations are built. Maslow's theory is that until more basal needs are met, we can't reach self-actualization.

grandparents, and friends to provide their free energy inputs to help in times of need. We can still utilize more new free energy by creating ordered gradients and enlisting others to help us in our cause.

When we begin to think in the paradigm of free energy and entropy, human needs and motivations become more clear. Figure 7.2 details a new theory of human motivation which is heavily influenced by Maslow's thinking. Physical needs such as food, water, and shelter make up the base of this pyramid. After these are met, humans will use available free energy for mental needs such as seeking safety, love, and esteem. Together, mental and physical needs can be thought of as somatic (related to the body) stewardship activities, where free energy is spent stewarding the self. After somatic needs are met, we can use any extra available free energy on extra-somatic stewardship. This includes stewardship activities such as cleaning, cooking, lawn care, repairs, mending, and childcare.

It's only after we use available free energy for somatic and extra-somatic stewardship, that we can use whatever available free energy is left for creation. Creation activities include starting businesses, creating social structures and laws, building new inventions, participating in scientific discovery, and conceiving new philosophies. A person with substantial inherited wealth will easily have enough free energy left over for creation. However, individuals without wealth won't always have enough free energy to spend on ambitious creative projects. Individuals without wealth will have to find a way to minimize the requirements for extra-somatic stewardship if they wish to spend a meaningful amount of free energy on creation.

I include this section here before fully diving into the section on stewardship to make an already obvious point more clear; not everyone has a moral obligation to create or steward. Only those with the appropriate free energy resources have this responsibility. If a person is struggling to find enough food or water to survive, they have no moral obligation to create or steward anything other than themselves. Creating and stewarding are privileges for those with adequate free energy resources to spend. In the next section,

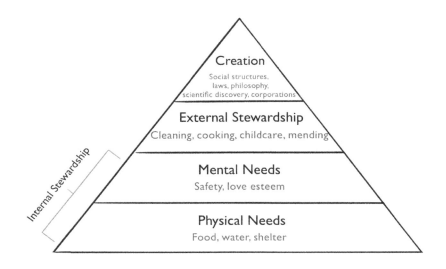

Figure 7.2. Free energy (usually in the form of money or time) must be first spent on securing our internal needs like food, water, and safety. After securing our internal needs, we can use available free energy for external stewardship. At the top of the free energy pyramid is creation. Not everyone has enough left over free energy to spend on creating, but those who do can spend it on things like starting businesses, making art, inventing, or even philosophizing.

I'll detail how to spend your free energy resources stewarding ordered gradients if you have the free energy means to do so.

Steward a Horseshoe Nail and Save a Kingdom

According to the logic of the entropic philosophy, conscious entities should be stewards of gradients because it would help slow the increase of entropy in our universe. One way of slowing the increase of entropy is creating ordered gradients with available free energy; the topic of chapter six. Creating gradients isn't the only way to slow down entropy's march. We can create another barrier by stewarding and preserving existing gradients.

To be good stewards:
- We should use free energy to lengthen the longevity of gradients that already exist.
- We should responsibly steward ordered gradients we create to ensure they don't inadvertently destroy other gradients.
- We should preserve the diversity of gradients in our universe.

In this section, we'll dive into the first bullet point on this list. *To be good stewards, we should use free energy to lengthen the longevity of gradients that already exist.* In essence, this means we should be fastidious in our efforts to maintain, repair, or otherwise steward existing gradients. Benjamin Franklin advocated for this same rigorous stewardship back in 1758 when he wrote the essay *The Way to Wealth.*

> *"For the want of a nail the shoe was lost,*
> *For the want of a shoe the horse was lost,*
> *For the want of a horse the rider was lost,*
> *For the want of a rider the battle was lost,*
> *For the want of a battle the kingdom was lost,*
> *And all for the want of a horseshoe-nail."*

This passage details what happens when we neglect to spend our personal free energy stewarding our possessions. Entropy can easily cascade and take down a kingdom if we neglect to input any free energy to steward and maintain our creations at the nail and horseshoe levels. According to the entropic philosophy, it's a moral imperative to steward your personal possessions.

This is because maintaining existing gradients takes less free energy than building a new gradient from nothing.

Up until the industrial revolution, the statement was painfully obvious to any common man. In Franklin's time for example, if a women's coat developed a hole in it, the path of least free energy use was to steward the coat by mending the hole. It would have required much more free energy in terms of time or money for the woman to fabricate a completely new garment herself or to buy a new one. Only the extremely wealthy, with an overflowing abundance of free energy, would have ever considered throwing the coat away and buying a new one. As far as a mass balance of free energy use is concerned, little has changed since the 1700s. It still takes more substantial free energy input to make a new coat than it does to steward and mend one that needs to be repaired.

How is it that modern man pays less money, yet uses more free energy for the same amenities as our ancestors? The answer is simple. *We do not pay the true free energy price for the free energy we take from our planet today.* Up until the industrial revolution, free energy prices were fixed. Our primary pool of free energy came from human and animal labor. For thousands of years, we only spent the free energy we could harness directly from ourselves and a few species of domesticated animals.

With human consciousness came access to stores of free energy beyond our evolutionary niche. Today we look at this access to stores of free energy in terms of fossil fuels, natural resources, and human labor as a bottomless inheritance – ours to spend and squander for the rest of human existence. But just like a real trust fund, it can run out. Our prodigal use of resources today reflects how we view the free energy available on our planet. We view it as infinite and thus place an extremely low monetary value on using the Earth's free energy stores. As we now well know, Earth's free energy stores are finite. As of now, we don't have access to free energy throughout our solar system or galaxy; all we have is what's right here on our home planet. If we overdraw on what we now have access to now, the evolutionary penalty will be the same as it's always been. Mother Earth may be shrewd, but at least she's predictable.

To be good stewards, we need to start paying the true price for the luxuries we enjoy today. Part of paying that price is taking responsibility for the ordered gradients we own. In order to conserve available free energy, we should repair possessions instead of buying new ones. If we must discard an object, we should do so in a way that doesn't harm or destroy other ordered gradients in the universe.

The Ownership Responsibility

Entropy ruthlessly abrades every physical possession we have. Maybe the most obvious example of this is our vehicles. The favorite car I ever owned was a 2011 Jeep Patriot. Me and this Jeep had some great times. Together, we went on rock-climbing trips across the country, explored logging roads in the Black Hills of South Dakota, and commuted in Chicago traffic to my first "real job" out of graduate school. I loved my Jeep and took care of it the best I could. I made sure to take care of the regular maintenance like oil changes, new wipers, fresh brake pads, and new tires.

After putting 100,000 miles on my Jeep, entropy started to win. The suspension needed major work, and it started having some issues with overheating. Minor maintenance stewardship wouldn't cut it anymore, and I decided to sell the car and pass on that ownership responsibility to someone else. A different owner would now be responsible for stewarding the Jeep and making sure entropy didn't prematurely claim the vehicle. Entropy makes us all stewards, whether we like it or not.

Stewarding our possession isn't just a necessity of modern life, it's also a moral imperative of the entropic philosophy. When entropy inevitably begins to wear away at the owner's object, it's the responsibility of the owner to expend the least amount of free energy required to mend and maintain the object. If the object becomes so damaged that it will require more free energy to repair than it would to create the same object anew, the owner may responsibly recycle or, in rare instances, discard the object and obtain a new one.

We struggle a great deal with this ownership responsibility today because many of us simply own more than we can efficiently steward, but it wasn't always this way. Our materialistic obsession with physical objects is new for *Homo sapiens*. For most of human history, we lived as hunter-gatherers who owned very few physical objects. Because of our nomadic nature, we couldn't own more than we could carry with us. There was a penalty in the form of caloric expenditure for owning too much and having to physically carry the load. About 10,000 years ago, with the advent of agriculture, we began to build more permanent dwellings that we began to fill with human artifacts. For most, these dwellings were still quite small. In ancient Egypt for example, small dwellings were made for entire families of mud and grasses that were only a few hundred square feet. Ancient Egyptians were on to the tiny house trend over 5,000 years ago.

The Victorian era in the late 1800s, famous for its large mansions, should be considered an architectural misnomer. Very few families could afford these huge mansions that began to spread in the early industrial revolution. As far as dwellings go, a better name for the late 1800s and early 1900s would be the tenement and farmhouse era. It's not as catchy or regal of a name, but it's more historically accurate. As a percentage of the whole population, very few families lived in the large Victorian mansions this period was named for.

It wasn't until after the second world war in 1945 that the middle class emerged. The post-World War II economic expansion resulted in higher wages, the rise of suburban living, and the rampant consumerism we still see today. See Table 7.1 for an overview of the average American home size since the 1950s. Directly following the end of World War II the average US home size was still below 1,000 sq. feet. Even though family size is shrinking, home square footage continues to balloon. Home sizes today are almost 200% bigger than before the post-war economic boom of the middle class. It wasn't until the 1950s and '60s that the middle class of the developed world started building bigger and bigger houses and filling their spaces with more and more stuff. I make this point to show how incredibly recent our obsession with owning physical objects is.

Date	Average US Home Size (sq. Feet)
1950's	950
1960's	1,100
1970's	1,350
2006	2,350
2015	2,700

Table 7.1: Average US home size by date showing a 184% increase in home size from the end of the second world war to present day.

Our big houses are filled with our possessions which we don't do a great job of stewarding. We're in a vicious consumeristic cycle of waste —Constantly discarding our possessions in favor of something newer, shinier, and less tarnished by entropy's unsightly effects. We have shirked the ownership responsibility of stewarding our possessions for many decades now. If we intend to start taking this responsibility seriously, we need to break out of our wasteful consumeristic cycles. Like trucker hats and gaucho pants, this consumeristic fad isn't a good look on *Homo sapiens*. I hope this recent cultural trend will fade into something more tasteful.

From Epicurus in 270 BC to today's Mari Kondo, we're told that owning excessive possessions can make us unhappy. There's a reason why owning too much makes us miserable. We can try to shirk our responsibility, but unless you have endless wealth, the burden of ownership eventually overpowers us. Reflect for a moment on how you spend your evenings and weekends. If you own a home, there's a good chance you spend much of your free time on home repairs, tending to the lawn, renovating, decorating, or landscaping. For many, we become so fatigued stewarding our big-ticket possessions like our home, vehicle, and electronics that we have little stewardship stamina left for the rest of our myriad nick-nacks. If the strap of a purse breaks, it's discarded or shoved in a closet corner. If a small kitchen appliance fails, we will toss it. Garages, closets, and basements fill up with items that lose their glimmer or need attention. Landfills, roadsides, and oceans are the receptacles for the items we choose to ignore forever.

All our stuff makes us miserable because we have become stewardship slaves to our possessions. Thinking back to the hierarchy of free energy use can help us put this in perspective. Owning too many possessions is a drain on our finite free energy. If we have too many things to steward, we can use up all our free energy on stewarding before getting to create anything. There are those whose excessive possessions cause misery, anxiety, and stress. The root of this misery stems from being unable to spend free energy on anything other than stewardship. Many of us yearn to create; to write the book we've talked about for years, to pick back up our bass guitar and make music again, to start the business we've always dreamed could be so successful. These dreams all take free energy to bring to fruition. Our consumption traps us in a stewardship role and saps our available free energy away from creating.

Consumerism wounds the human spirit by depriving it of the joys of creation. Consumerism can stop us from reaching the apex of the free energy use pyramid. This is because being a consumer means you're committing a large portion, if not all, of your available free energy to stewardship of physical objects. Our excessive consumption robs us of free energy that we could spend creating. There's a trade-off we make when we dedicate free energy to stewardship; it comes at the expense of free energy we could have spent creating. If you're unable to write your book, start your band, paint your masterpiece, or found your company, the reason isn't solely in your mind. It may be what's in your garage, closet, backyard, and basement that's sapping your creativity.

For most of us, becoming better stewards means owning far less than we do today. To fulfill the ownership responsibility, it's a moral imperative to only own what you can effectively steward. A result of taking our responsibility more seriously is becoming more judicious about the products we choose to own. See Figure 7.3 for a flow chart showing the most ethical process for stewarding possession. When we buy an object or accept a gift, we need to look at this transaction as contractual. By purchasing an object or accepting a gift, we have now signed on the dotted line to take on the ownership responsibility for our new possession.

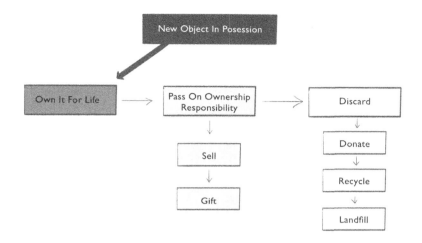

Figure 7.3 is a flow chart depicting the most ethical way to steward a product from a new purchase to the end of its useful life. The bolded arrow denotes that the preferred path is to own an object for life. However, the ownership responsibility can also be passed on via selling or gifting an object. The least ethical path is to discard an object. If you must discard an object, it should first be donated then recycled. Only the most damaged products that cannot be salvaged should end up in a landfill.

Taking this life-long stewardship responsibility runs seriously counter to our modern hyper-consumerist culture. We buy objects that we intend to use only once or twice before sending them straight to the landfill. To become better stewards of our belongings, we need to change our mindset about what it means to purchase a new object. Today, we buy something with the intent to own it only for as long as it serves our mercurial whims. This mindset needs to change. We should buy something with the intent to own it for life. Often, these objects will be of higher quality and as a result, will be more expensive than objects meant to end up in landfills. As a positive side effect, these quality objects will be more durable and require less of our free energy to steward.

It's not just individuals that have this responsibility. Governments and corporations have the same responsibilities as conscious entities to take the stewardship responsibility seriously. If we want to be better stewards, the onus is on us to choose to purchase fewer, higher-quality objects and own them for as long as possible. Doing this ensures that we preserve available free energy use, and destroy the least amount of existing ordered gradients on our planet.

Stewarding The Human Body

As we age, there's a physical object most of us spend more and more time having to steward. Many of us spend more time and money on this object than we do on our homes, cars, or wardrobe. The paramount stewardship responsibility we have is to ourselves and our own human bodies. It's easy to forget that our conscious minds are intertwined with meaty physical bodies that are subject to the laws of thermodynamics.

In part, this simple truth is so easy to forget because for most of human history we lacked the knowledge and free energy access required to steward our bodies. Without knowledge and free energy, we prayed to a god we hoped had the entropy antidote when we fell ill or became injured. Shamans and priests claimed to be conduits of the healing free energy held by god. Human progress and scientific advances have called for a referendum on these claims.

For those in developed countries, the verdict is clear. When we fall ill, the priest is now who we visit second after we consult with a modern medical doctor. This very action of even the most religious among us in the developed world shows that we now believe more in the knowledge and free energy access of man than we do of god.

Unlike faith healing, there is good reason to believe that man is acquiring both the knowledge and free energy access required to effectively heal ourselves of the ailments imposed on us by entropy. In the last 100 years, we've discovered genes and invented genetic engineering tools; offering the first cures to some of the known thousands of genetic diseases. We've come to understand the function and material makeup of most internal organs, and have begun engineering lab-grown replacements for failed bits and pieces. We discovered computer science and have since devised algorithms that can predict an illness before it strikes us down. Our current biomedical revolution lies at the nexus of our newfound knowledge and free energy access.

It seems that knowledge, and not free energy, is the current limiting factor in extending human longevity. We now have access to countless zettajoules of free energy; much more than would be needed to offset the effects of entropy on a single human body to extend its life a few extra decades. The free energy is there, and yet this seemingly simple energetic feat has not been accomplished. Take an automobile for example: When a car breaks, we have sufficient knowledge and free energy access to fix whatever is needed. Given enough free energy inputs, there's no reason a vehicle couldn't last centuries. Human bodies are not so different from other physical matter like cars as far as entropy is concerned. Our free energy inputs can heal the sick, but we have yet to extend our lifespans beyond the normal upper limits of life expectancy that nature granted to our hunter-gatherer ancestors.

When we finally attain the level of knowledge required, our consciousness has already unlocked the key to eternal youth. Our consciousness granted us the ability to seek free energy outside of the niche we evolved in. We can use this free energy to steward the physical human body when our knowledge eventually catches up to our free energy access.

Even with access to all the free energy in our galaxy, we can't live forever. It's not even truly possible for us to ever completely eradicate and cure cancer. The tug of entropy will always try to pull our genetic code into randomness. The effects of UV light, common environmental chemicals, and random DNA transcription errors will occur no matter how much access to free energy and how much knowledge we have. There's no cure for entropy and there is no stopping it from meddling with our genetic code. But just because we can't cure cancer, doesn't mean we can't leverage our knowledge and free energy access to slow it down and fix genetic errors as soon as they crop up. We can't eradicate cancerous genetic transcription errors, but we can apply free energy such that the cancer is temporarily "cured"; at least until entropy strikes our nucleotides again. We can't live forever, but there's no thermodynamic reason why we can't live to be hundreds or even thousands of years old.

If we were to harness all the free energy in our universe, there's no scientific reason why we can't live 99.9% as long as the universe. As long as there is free energy available, we could use it to steward and extend a human life. Thermodynamically speaking, a human body could last not just thousands of years, but millions or even billions of years. Like the ship of Theseus[21], we could repair ourselves, fiber by fiber, cell by cell, and even protein by protein for aeons.

Our bodies are temples inhabited by the only known conscious beings in the whole of the universe. As we've touched on, other life on earth should be protected and stewarded, but human life does deserve special considerations. According to the entropic philosophy, we must steward ourselves and take care of our physical incarnations. As conscious entities, we have a responsibility to steward our bodies by nurturing our health and longevity with preventative, healing, and mindful free energy inputs.

Stewarding Diversity

In the preceding chapter we talked about the importance of creating diversity, but that's just half the picture. To be the most

---

[21] Of course, this raises all the same philosophical questions as the ship of Theseus. If both our body and mind have changed and warped many times over a billion years, what does it mean to be "you"?

effective Entropians, we also need to preserve diversity. In the previous chapter, we discussed how diversity is an effective tool of evolution by natural selection to slow the increase of entropy. This is a justification for creating more diversity, and it's also a justification for why we must preserve diversity that's already been created.

Biomass and biodiversity are two ways to measure how much life is on our planet. Biomass is something we can measure and get a number for. Cut down all the aspen on one acre of land and weigh it. What the scale reads off is the biomass of aspen trees on that acre of land. Biomass is one way to measure the amount of biological gradients on earth. Over time, increasing biomass would be selected for on Earth and Earth-like planets and this is just what we've seen happen. Life on Earth probably started as a few proto-cells in hydrothermal deep ocean vents. These protocells evolved into simple celled bacteria (or prokaryotes) as they grew to occupy more niches. More complex cells (eukaryotes) later evolved and grew to occupy new niches. Eukaryotes gave rise to entire kingdoms of life such as plants, fungi, and animals. The biomass of life on earth started with just a few protocells in hydrothermal vents which has now grown into the 550 gigatons of life on Earth today[22]. If all the biomass on Earth was embodied in nothing but African bush elephants, we would have enough elephants to build a stacked elephant bridge from here to Mars. In fact, we'd have just

---

[22] *The biomass distribution on Earth.* Yinon M. Bar-On, Rob Phillips, Ron Milo. Proceedings of the National Academy of Sciences. Jun 2018

enough to build our bridge three elephants deep. Are you taking notes on this, Elon Musk?

Biomass on our planet has been increasing over time. Biodiversity, otherwise known as the number of species on Earth, is the key that allows biomass to keep expanding and growing. The creation of new species creates new niches. When a new niche opens up, a new species can evolve to fill it. Undisturbed by catastrophe or major disturbance, this cycle of creation only begets more creation. This is what we've seen on Earth starting with a handful of protocells in hydrothermal vents, up to the present day 550 gigatons of biomass.

As we covered in the last chapter on creation, over the long run diversity is a good evolutionary bet. The Earth can get pummeled with asteroids and have mega volcanoes explode, but life has always been able to bounce back and flourish as new niches are again created and filled from the initial stock of survivors. While diversity is a stable long-term bet, it can be very volatile in the short term. That volatility comes from how these niches of available free energy are intertwined and built on top of each other.

Ecologists call these intertwined dependencies a food web, but they could just as well be called a free energy web. To understand just how interdependent the diversity of life on earth is, consider the kelp forests off of coastal Alaska. This food web can be broken up into three trophic levels (or food levels). The bottom trophic level is made up of the primary producers – in this case, the kelp and algae. The next trophic level up is the primary consumers who feed off of the primary producers. In this diagram, sea urchins are one of the primary consumers that feed on kelp. Sea otters are considered secondary consumers because they feed on sea urchins.

In food webs like this one, if populations of any one species are affected, these effects can cascade and wreak havoc on all species in the network. This is exactly what happened in the early 1900s as the expanding fur trade devastated the Alaskan sea otter population. With the sea otter populations suffering, sea urchin populations exploded in

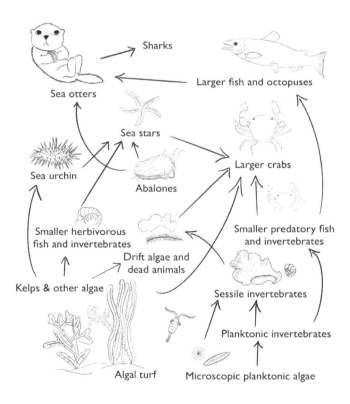

Figure 7.4. A free energy web diagram showing species interactions for a coastal Alaskan habitat.

the absence of predation. The unregulated urchin army overcame the kelp forest by overgrazing and eventually caused the kelp forest to nearly collapse.

Diversity is fragile. Take away a few otters, and the entire kelp forest can vanish. This is why we must take special care to protect the diversity of life on Earth. We're in the middle of an extinction crisis, with species dying off at 100 to 1,000 times the normal rate, but it's not just extinction we need to protect against. The Alaskan otters didn't go extinct. All it took to devastate the ecosystem was to throw off their population numbers. Given how delicate and fragile diversity is, we need to take special care to protect it. Without diversity, biomass levels drop. Less biomass means less self-replicating, self- colonizing ordered gradients in the universe. This is how protecting biodiversity helps us achieve the aims of the entropic philosophy.

Thinking more broadly, we need to protect the diversity of our universe as well. As we covered in the intergalactic field trip thought experiment, we live in a universe full of diverse shapes, sizes, and densities. As our free energy access grows, we need to ensure we protect the diversity that already exists beyond our planet as well.

...

I'm not the first person to use universal Darwinism as a tool to form a new philosophy. Unfortunately, Darwinism and philosophy have a regrettable history rife with misunderstanding. Many throughout history have bent science to form a justification for their racist, bigoted, and logically corrupt ideologies. Maybe the worst offender of this in history is Adolf Hitler. Hitler saw the world in terms of "survival of the fittest" and viewed white men as being the fittest. This is incorrect.

We now well know that white men are not the fittest race of humans. We now know there's no "fittest race" or master race of humans at all. This is what evolution and history have truly come to tell us. For students of evolution and history unclouded by ego, greed, and xenophobia, this is an accepted truth. Evolution by natural selection tells us that the master race is *the entire human race*. Evolution has shaped us over time to be as diverse as the habitats we humans came to live in. This diversity is what's selected for. It's not just biodiversity we should seek to preserve; the entropic philosophy tells us that we have a moral obligation to also preserve and celebrate human diversity.

The subjugation of man doesn't have a basis in evolution or science. Like so many regrettable and tragic stories in history, the commonality seems to be human greed. Greed is something all men and women on Earth seem to struggle with. If anything, our evolution has guided us to personally desire more and more free energy for ourselves. In the next chapter, we'll explore where to draw the line and decide when enough is enough.

Chapter Summary

- The second moral imperative of the entropic philosophy is to steward.

- The current paradigm of environmental ethics offers no logic-based reasoning to steward and has been ineffective at persuading us to take action.

- Maslow's hierarchy of needs can be adapted to describe how we humans use free energy to steward and create.

- To be good stewards:

- We should use free energy to lengthen the longevity of gradients that already exist.

- We should responsibly steward ordered gradients we create to ensure they don't inadvertently destroy other gradients.

- We should preserve the diversity of gradients in our universe.

8

Conserve

"The wealth required by nature is limited and is easy to procure; but the wealth required by vain ideals extends to infinity."

— Epicurus

THE UNITED STATES Declaration of Independence asserts that every person in the country has the right to life, liberty, and the pursuit of happiness. This document may have been written in 1776, but its roots date back to 250 BC. One of the authors of this document, Thomas Jefferson, was an Epicurean, meaning that he followed the philosophical teachings of Epicurus. He shared the company of other notable historical figures with a similar mind such as John Lock, Thomas Hobbes, David Hume, and Adam Smith who all cite inspiration from the same philosophical teachings.

Epicurus was a philosopher with a lot to say about how to be happy. Epicureans are hedonists, meaning that they see the purpose of life as seeking pleasure. For the Epicurean sect of hedonists, this doesn't mean endless orgies or being fanned with a palm leaf while eating exotic fruits. This ancient philosopher discovered that being a hedonist could be something quite different. Epicurus was the original minimalist. It's said that he only possessed two cloaks and that his diet consisted almost solely of bread, olives, and the occasional morsel of cheese. This philosophy can be boiled down to the following statement: Find pleasure in life's simple joys. Epicurus teaches, the less you want, the happier you'll be with what you have.

As a holistic philosophy, Epicureanism leaves a lot to be desired. As we discussed at length in the first chapter, with all we know about the universe it seems unbelievable to put human happiness squarely at the center of everything. The entropic philosophy gives a much more realistic and accurate description of the world and a new moral compass that always points the same direction whether a human being is there to look at it or not.

The ethics and metaphysics of Epicureanism are lacking, but we can still pick out a few relevant gems. Epicureanism as a philosophy is far from perfect, but it's still extremely useful to us as a tool to achieve happiness. Specifically, it's a great tool to achieve human happiness while using the fewest resources possible. The two go hand in hand with the entropic philosophy being the guiding reason why, and Epicureanism being one possible means to this end.

In the last 200 years, we have enjoyed more luxuries than ever before, but it doesn't seem to be making us any happier. A quick study of history shows us a very clear trend. Luxuries don't last long before becoming reclassified as basic necessities. We quickly get used to new comforts and assimilate these into the category of basic human needs. Take travel for example; in the early 19th century, it was very difficult for the average American to travel more than a few miles away from their home. Flash forward 200 years to the present day, and global travel is now considered a basic necessity by many. Long-distance domestic travel is no longer a rare luxury, it's a necessity to see family, go to weddings, and take summer vacations. In the last 200 years, many things have transitioned from extravagant luxury to basic need including exotic foods, confections, travel, recreational sports, entertainment, brand new home furnishings, automobiles, and beauty treatments. All of these things would have been luxurious to someone 200 years ago, but are now considered basic needs by every middle-class earner. We've gained more and more luxuries and material possessions in the last 200 years, but it doesn't seem to be making us happier. It certainly doesn't seem to be satiating our desires as we continue to consume more and more.

The central reason why we need to be happy with less is because of a simple fact of physics; free energy in our universe is finite. Despite what proceeding generations may have thought, resources and free energy here on Earth are limited and we can indeed use them up. This idea is not a sentiment of environmentalist woo – It's a foundational principle of process engineering. Biological life, the mechanism that evolved on our planet to store free energy, evolved to use the least amount of resources possible and to recycle most materials. Figure 8.1 can help us understand why this is so.

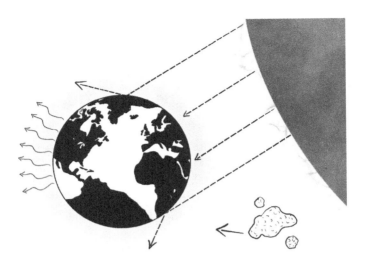

Figure 8.1 shows the inputs and outputs of our planet as a mass balance. Inputs include free energy from the sun in the form of photons and physical matter in the form of asteroids and meteors. Outputs include radiated photons not absorbed by Earth's surface and atmospheric gasses lost to space.

As we can see in figure 8.1, we do have some inputs of free energy and physical matter from the sun and space rocks entering our atmosphere. We also have physical matter and free energy exiting Earth's system in the form of radiated photons and the loss of atmospheric gasses to space. So it's true that as long as the sun and earth exist together, free energy will be available on Earth's surface. This constant influx of free energy from the sun does not give us a free pass to use up other free energy stores here on Earth. The solar gradient is abundant for now, but other gradients on our planet are finite and being depleted quickly.

Anytime we disperse and break up pools of statistically unlikely gradients of matter, we are using free energy and causing entropy to increase. Take helium for example. Helium exists naturally here on earth from uranium and thorium decay in the Earth's crust. This decay leaves pockets of helium that can be mined, often near natural gas deposits. If we look back at Figure 8.1, when we mine and use the helium, it mostly still stays here on Earth with only a very small percentage escaping Earth's atmosphere. Even though most of the helium is still here on Earth, that doesn't mean that it's still usable. After we mine helium, use it, and release it into the atmosphere, it's almost thermodynamically impossible to recollect enough of it to use again. Picking individual helium particles out of our atmosphere to recollect for use would be like thoroughly mixing in a handful of salt grains into an entire beachfront and then trying to get the salt back out in a pure form. It's technically possible, but not at all energetically favorable to do. For that reason, when we use all the Helium on Earth stored in these nice, easy-to-use, statistically unlikely gradients in our planet's crust, the Helium on Earth is effectively gone. We'll likely need helium to help us get off-planet and survive there. Helium is used for medical imaging, scientific research, manufacturing fiber optic cables, semiconductor manufacturing, rocket launches, and welding. It's not just helium this concept applies to. We are butting up against the same problem with nickel, copper, lithium, cobalt, and many other rare earth minerals.

It's true that in Figure 8.1, very little helium, nickel, copper, and cobalt are escaping the open system of our planet. However, what we're seeing is the second law of thermodynamics at play. These important resources, once condensed and easy to use, are becoming randomly dispersed across our land and air. It will be extremely energetically unfavorable for us to attempt recovery of these resources once they're spent. What's more, almost no new usable resources are entering our system. For this reason, we need to treat our resources on Earth as finite and act accordingly to achieve our goals of creating and stewarding ordered gradients at a large scale.

It's not just our planet this applies to; free energy in the universe is also finite. This concept of the universe reaching thermodynamic equilibrium (max entropy) is a core concept in the thought experiment behind the entropic philosophy. We as humans, with our cosmically fleeting lifespans, tend to forget this glaring truth. Free energy gradients on Earth won't last forever. Free energy from our sun won't even last forever. Eventually, all the free energy in our universe will run out as the cosmos age into maximal disorder. With this deep-time perspective, it becomes apparent that we must do all we can to conserve free energy gradients both on our home planet and beyond.

Using the Cheapest Free Energy First

When Josiah Willard Gibbs coined the term free energy, he didn't take one very important fact into account: *life cannot exist without free energy*. This makes the term free energy quite the misnomer. Specifically, the word *free* in the name free energy is very misleading. Since all life in the universe relies on free energy to sustain and replicate, free energy is the only true thing of value to any form of life. Once the free energy runs out, there will be no way to sustain life in the universe any longer. It doesn't make much sense to call the only real resource of value to life "free".

It's also misleading to use the term "free" when referring to free energy, because it implies that all free energy use incurs the same cost – nothing. This is not true. Some free energy is much more expensive to use than others. For example, the total free energy expenditure associated with fossil fuels differs greatly from the free energy expenditure of using solar energy. Remember that anytime a gradient is turned into a random discorded mess, free energy is destroyed and entropy increases.

Consider the amount of free energy destroyed when gasoline is used. Fossil fuels themselves are ordered gradients. When we burn fossil fuels, the ordered gradients of connected carbon break up into individual molecules of carbon in the form of CO_2. This is not the only free energy cost incurred from using fossil fuels. In the case of gasoline, free energy was also destroyed in the process of mining, transporting, and refining this fuel source before it was even used in a combustion engine. Looking first at crude oil extraction; free energy is used in the production of mining equipment. Free energy is also destroyed via the extraction and mining process whereby the natural landscape becomes more disordered. In the case of the 2010 BP oil spill in the Gulf of Mexico, substantial free energy was further destroyed by releasing oil into the ocean and shoreline which destroyed the habitat of countless species and killed an untold number of living organisms. After the crude oil is extracted, it needs to be transported to a refinery. Transportation itself uses available free energy, but so does creating the transportation infrastructure. Laying railroad tracks, building roads, and placing pipelines destroy free energy in the form of natural habitats. The process of refining crude oil into gasoline also takes free energy, usually in the form of more fossil fuels! The free energy destruction doesn't stop once the gasoline leaves the exhaust pipe as CO_2. The increasing CO_2 levels are causing rapid climate change and ocean acidification which is a contributing factor to the current mass extinction of life on Earth- a very expensive free energy cost indeed as the ordered gradients embodied in life decays away.

As we can see from looking at this process end-to-end, it's not just the free energy in the carbon-carbon bonds of gasoline we use when burning fossil fuels, there are many other free energy costs incurred along the way. When we sum up all the free energy costs spent to mine, refine, transport, and pollute using fossil fuels we can begin to understand just how expensive this source of free energy really is.

Solar power is a much cheaper free energy source when compared to the price point of fossil fuels. Solar energy is cheaper than fossil fuels for two main reasons. The first is that even when we account for the free energy used to produce and install solar panels, we still come out ahead on the free energy balance sheet[23]. Silicon, a semiconductor, is the main material used on solar panels

---

[23] Admittedly, this is something I could quantify further using actual numbers and equations. This calculation is something that will likely be included in the second edition of this book. Even without the mathematical quantification, we can still take a mental tally of the moving pieces here and see that solar energy is the cheaper free energy source.

to capture free energy from the sun. Unlike crude oil, silica is extremely abundant on Earth. It's the second most common element found on the surface of our planet after oxygen. According to the USGS, silica mining has a limited environmental impact. While the open-pit mining of silica does destroy some natural habitats, the environmental impacts of silica mining pale in comparison to the environmental destruction incurred from crude oil extraction. The second reason solar power is cheaper is because free energy rains down on Earth whether a human being is there to collect it or not. The same isn't true for fossil fuels. The only reason free energy has been released from the carbon-carbon bonds of oil is because of human activity on Earth. If no humans were around, the free energy stored in the statistically unlikely molecular bonds on fossil fuels would slowly break over time due to slow, natural, oxidation. These carbon bonds would have remained unbroken for millions, if not billions, of years if it weren't for human interference.

Refusing free energy from the sun in favor of using fossil fuels is akin to a person on the brink of dehydration standing in the pouring rain refusing to drink the falling water – instead remaining thirsty while digging for an aquifer. *Homo sapiens* is a species thirsty for free energy. The good news is, if we choose the right cup, we have an abundant fountain to drink from. Figure 8.2 shows the relative prices we'll pay to fill our cup depending on the free energy source. The entropic philosophy advocates for using the least free energy possible.

If humans can become more technologically advanced and work our way up the Kardashev Scale, we will increasingly use solar power over other free energy sources. Sci-fi authors and physicists have told us this for decades. The conceptual inventor of the Dyson sphere first pointed this out almost 100 years ago. In his 1937 sci-fi work, *Star Maker*, Olaf Stapledon conceived of a technologically advanced race that was able to capture all the free energy from a star. It wasn't until 1960 that Freeman Dyson published his thought experiment proposing that such a device would be theoretically possible. Like a pebble in a locket, Dyson envisioned

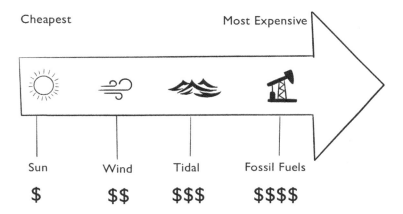

Figure 8.2 shows the decreasing relative cost of different free energy sources. Fossil fuels are the most expensive source of free energy. Tidal and wind are cheaper than fossil fuels. Tidal is more expensive than wind because the tidal energy generators are built in fragile coastal marine environments and the turbines would likely be made from steel and copper. Wind is slightly preferred over tidal because the environmental impact of widespread wind turbines would likely be lower than that of widespread tidal turbines. Solar power is the cheapest free energy source.

a shell built around a star that could capture its entire free energy output.

For our current level of technological sophistication, the transition to solar energy now is the right choice. However, after advancing further on the Kardashev scale we may find other sources of free energy in our universe that are cheaper to harvest. Many physicists, including Steven Hawking, have theorized how we might harness free energy from a black hole. There may even be opportunities for us to harness free energy at the subatomic and particulate levels via matter-antimatter annihilation. It's now thought that the matter and energy we're currently able to observe and study in physics only account for 5% of our universe. The other 95% of our universe may be embodied in the form of dark energy and dark matter that we are currently not able to study, let alone tap into as an energy source. The possible free energy obtained from this mysterious 95% of our universe may be the cheapest of all.

While this is fun to theorize about, we don't yet have access to these forms of free energy. We're not even a true type one civilization yet. If we want a shot at space colonization, then we need to focus on capturing cheap and available free energy from the sun. Our cup runs over with available free energy if we choose to drink from the well of our cosmic endowment.

...

The more the human population grows, on Earth and beyond, we need to make sure our individual choices don't add up to a collective explosion. To understand how important this is, it's useful to illustrate just how much the human population could grow if we're able to capture a significant amount of free energy in our universe. Nick Bostrom already lays out this calculation for what he calls our cosmic endowment, in his 2014 book, *Superintelligence: Paths, Dangers, Strategies*.

"Consider a technologically mature civilization capable of building sophisticated [self-replicating, autonomous] Von Neumann probes. At 99% of c [the speed of light], they could reach some $2x10^{20}$ stars. These travel speeds are energetically attainable using a small fraction of the resources available in the solar system...If we assume that 10% of stars have a planet that is suitable for habitation by human-like creatures, and that it could then be home to a population of a billion individuals for a billion years (with a human life lasting a century), this suggests that around 10^{35} human lives could be created in the future by an Earth-originating intelligent civilization."

For those not well-versed in scientific notation 10^{35} humans is 1,000,000,000,000,000,000,000,000,000,000,000,000. This is a number so big, that our human minds can't well conceptualize what it means, but we don't need to get to 10^{35} humans before our collective action adds up in a meaningful way. The seven billion humans currently on Earth are already having a dramatic impact on the ordered gradients on our planet. There are other considerations for planets we colonize with no life (such as the plastic Pluto example), but here on Earth, we need to protect existing gradients. We also need to protect the free energy endowment on our planet and ensure we save enough of it to help us colonize space. The following are an incomplete set of recommendations for things every conscious entity can start implementing to ensure we conserve the free energy on planet Earth. The section below doesn't just apply to individual humans, it applies to governments and corporations as well. That said, I don't believe implementing these changes is an exhaustive list or panacea for our culturally conspicuous free energy consumption, but what's outlined below is a good start.

Minimalism

Minimalism might seem a counter-intuitive way to meet the main objective of the entropic philosophy – To use available free energy in the universe to create ordered gradients to slow the increase of entropy. How could creating and owning *less* order possibly help us achieve this? It's true that as we colonize other planets, minimalism won't always apply[24]. However, given our current circumstances on Earth, minimalism applies in the short term to help us achieve our goal to create cosmically meaningful gradients in the long term. If we want to achieve this future goal, we need to make a few changes including:

---

[24] It will still probably apply on planets where we create ecosystems of other lifeforms. It doesn't apply in cases such as the plastic Pluto example where there are no dynamic self-replicating ordered gradients to destroy with static gradients like single-use plastics

- Stop destroying biological gradients with pollution and waste
- Conserve available free energy on our planet to ensure we can spend part of our planetary free energy endowment on colonizing space
- Switch from expensive free energy like fossil fuel to cheaper free energy such as solar power

Adopting the practice of minimalism will, in part, help us achieve these goals in the long term. Owning fewer physical objects is an obvious way to minimize individual free energy consumption. The last chapter made the case that if you can't steward it, you shouldn't buy it. Stewarding within your means is one reason to be a minimalist, but it's not the only reason according to the entropic philosophy. Owning fewer physical objects will also help conserve free energy on Earth and buy us more time to solve the mass (im)balance problem shown in Figure 8.1.

Consider the free energy consumption associated with owning a vehicle. There's the free energy expenditure of environmental damage from the mining and extraction of the raw materials needed to make the car. Next, there's the free energy used to manufacture and transport the vehicle to a dealer. Then there's the free energy required after the vehicle is purchased to fuel the vehicle and the free energy required to keep the car in good repair. Lastly, there's the free energy cost from the environmental damage incurred from disposing of the vehicle. Vehicles are one example of free energy-intensive possessions. Big houses, excessive clothing, and home furnishings are examples of other free energy-intensive objects.

Until we put better systems in place to protect the environment and other life on Earth and until we make the switch from expensive fossil fuels to cheaper solar energy, we need to make some changes. Most notably is probably the change we need to make to drastically reduce our free energy consumption in the form of material possessions.

Minimalism does not advocate for self-deprivation or ultra-spartan resource use. Minimalism, combined with Epicurean teachings, is a tool to help us achieve a state of contentment and happiness by using the least amount of resources possible. At least in the short term, we need to cut our resource consumption if we hope to work towards the long-term goals laid out in the entropic philosophy.

Sharing

If the goal is to use our available resources as efficiently as possible, we need to take an honest inventory of what resources are being wasted. For most of us, we can look around our homes and find many things that are seldom, if ever, used. Despite being rarely deployed, we don't want to get rid of these items *just in case* we need them in the future. What about that picnic basket filled with outdoor-specific cutlery and dishes? I haven't been on a picnic in over 10 years, but maybe I'll use it again this summer. Better keep it *just in case*. That lathe sitting in the garage that hasn't been used for a woodworking project in the last 5 years? Who knows what projects I'll come up with next. Better keep it *just in case*. This "just in case" way of thinking is cluttering our homes, causing overconsumption, and is an inefficient way to use our limited resources. Being smarter about our resources doesn't mean we can't ever go on picnics or start a new woodworking project. Being smarter about our resources means we will have to start sharing if we want to keep up our standard of living.

After reading the chapter on stewardship, we should all be eager to reduce our personal stewardship burden. Under the new paradigm of the entropic philosophy, we should all prefer *access over ownership*. Access without the burden of ownership is what the emerging sharing economy promises. Why *own* a car that sits dormant 95% of the time when you can have *access* to a car for that 5% that you actually need it? This is what the future of ride-sharing offers.

We can share more than just our vehicles. Clothing is another resource that's being wasted. New companies that offer access to clothing through rentals are helping to solve this problem. It's wasteful to buy a garment for a special occasion and only wear it once or twice. With the artificially cheap price of clothing, many of us buy garments we wear only a few times. It's better for the individual and for our planet for people to rent this type of clothing rather than buying it and quickly discarding it. There are many other types of companies offering services such as music and media subscriptions, seasonal decoration rental, children's toy rentals, power tool rentals, and outdoor gear rentals.

The capitalist sharing economy isn't all we should rely on to better leverage our existing resources. As a culture, we need to be able to share with our friends, our family, our neighbors, and our community. This is something humanity figured out a long time ago, but only very recently seems to have forgotten. The BaYaka culture that thrived for tens of thousands of years in the Congo Basin up until the 1990s is one example of a culture that mastered sharing. According to an article in the May 2020 issues of the Scientific American *"The BaYaka economy is based on the principle that if you see someone with something you want, you simply ask for it. The BaYaka vociferously reject the idea that the natural world can be owned."* Many tribal cultures throughout human history have mastered this extreme kind of sharing, called a demand-sharing economy by anthropologists. The BaYaka and other demand-sharing cultures represent one extreme end of a spectrum where everything is shared fluidly and nothing is owned. Modern western culture represents the complete opposite end of the spectrum where almost nothing is shared and everything is owned by the individual. The entropic philosophy advocates that we find some middle ground on this spectrum that allows us to better leverage resources, and as a nice byproduct of this, get back to living in a supportive, caring community.

Free Energy Optimized Food

Eating is one of the most environmentally damaging and free energy intensive things we as humans do. Even small populations of hunter-gatherers had a profoundly negative impact on local megafauna. Human hunting played a large role in the wooly mammoth and giant sloth extinctions. There's no one smoking gun responsible for the current mass extinction. There are many factors (many of them human in origin) playing a role in the extinction crisis, but it's not gun smoke we should be looking for. The damning evidence is in the smoke billowing from grills, BBQ pits, and kitchen ranges. If we want to conserve the free energy on our planet, we need to drastically rethink our food and how we sustain the seven billion *Homo sapiens* on our planet.

An ideal Entropian diet would optimize for the maximum number of calories delivered to our stomachs in exchange for the least amount of free energy expenditure. Remember, free energy and energy (calories) are not the same thing[25]. The average western diet is not at all optimized for feeding us the most calories for the least amount of free energy. The average American eats three times more meat than the average of the rest of the world. With our current agricultural processes, eating meat is much more free energy intensive than eating a plant-based diet. Until agricultural innovations make meat more free energy friendly, the world needs to fill its plate with more plants and less animals.

As a food source, meat is not as free energy efficient as plants for several reasons. Meat production and transportation uses more fossil fuels, more land space, more water, and pollutes more than plant food production. Our meat-based agriculture system is incredibly resource-intensive. Today, 43% of the world's land area is used for agriculture (omitting terrestrial areas covered in ice or

---

[25] Calories are a form of energy. Statistically unlikely gradients are a form of free energy. Calories are not a measure of free energy. Calories are a form of energy. Remember, energy is conserved in our universe ($E=MC^2$). Free energy (exergy) is gradually used up until the universe reaches thermodynamic equilibrium.

desert). If we stopped eating meat, we would reclaim almost 13 million square miles of land. For reference, the continent of Africa is about 11.7 million square miles. We could have an entire continent's worth of land back, and then some, to restore natural habitat. We can achieve the same caloric and nutritional requirements needed to maintain homeostasis by eating plants instead of animals – and we should. If the goal is to conserve our free energy and use it efficiently, a plant-based diet is currently our best option.

It's not just what we eat that's causing this problem. How we eat is just as wasteful and inefficient from a free energy perspective. Specifically, the free energy we use on transporting food is exceptionally prodigal. About 10% of the carbon emission associated with food production comes from food transportation. This number makes sense when you consider the average distance traveled from "farm to table" in America is over 1,500 miles. Changing to a plant-based diet will have a much larger impact on climate change and habitat destruction, but switching to a more locally sourced diet will still help in optimizing our free energy use.

Avoiding plastic shrouded food will also help optimize our food intake and free energy use. As previously discussed, the eventual goal is to stop making single-use plastics on Earth (Pluto be damned). This is because plastic is destroying free energy tied up in natural landscapes, natural resources, and the delicate ecology of biological life. If we want to get there, then we each have an individual responsibility to stop buying it and using it. Food packaging is the leading source of single-use plastics. If food must be packaged, paper and other biodegradable, and bio-safe materials are far preferred to plastic packaging.

Changing our diet, eating locally produced food, and avoiding plastic packaging are all things individuals can do to optimize their personal free energy use. However, our biggest free energy optimization gains can only be realized by cooperating at the global systemic level. Agricultural practices and levels of pollution vary greatly between countries and even within a single country. At the process level, we can optimize our free energy use by being more precise with fertilization applications, not growing water-intensive crops in arid or semi-arid environments, and figuring out how to produce more food near major urban areas. Implementing processes that make sure food gets eaten and not wasted is another necessary step to optimizing our free energy use. In the United States, nearly 40% of all food produced is wasted. If we want to do better at conserving available free energy on our planet, making sure we actually eat the food we produce is a very good place to start.

...

According to the entropic philosophy, there's no moral shame in being rich. In fact, if you follow the moral guideposts laid out in the last three chapters to create, steward, and conserve, a very likely outcome of these combined behaviors is the accumulation of wealth. The entire human economy is based on paying money in exchange for individual free energy expenditure. If you spend your free energy creating a new product, masterpiece, or invention that provides value to others, you'll receive money for this. If you spend your free energy stewarding the home, car, or property of a stranger, you most certainly expect to be paid. If personal free energy is expended to create or steward your own possessions, this will save money that would have otherwise been spent paying for someone else's free energy.

Like many of our religions, The entropic philosophy offers a promise of prosperity for those who follow its moral teachings. The moral imperatives to create, steward, and conserve can culminate in an individual reward. As we'll see in the next chapter, this isn't the only similarity The entropic philosophy bears to ancient religions and other moral ideologies. Next, we'll explore why our religions, philosophies, and traditions all bear so many similarities to the entropic philosophy and begin to understand where our ancient intuitions and modern logic part ways.

Chapter Summary

- The third moral imperative of the entropic philosophy is to conserve.

- Free energy (exergy) in the universe will one day be completely used up. We should conserve it so future life can thrive.

- The long-term goals of the entropic philosophy require us to take short-term actions to ration some of the limited gradients on our planet. Rationing these gradients ensures we can colonize the cosmos and claim our cosmic endowment of free energy.

Part III

Entropia

9

Entropic Intuitions

ON THE EVENING of April 15th 2019, The roof of the Notre Dame cathedral in Paris erupted in flames. Billows of gray smoke engulfed the church as the fire spread, creeping towards the iconic gothic spire. Onlookers watched as the spire of Notre Dame was consumed by flames and eventually crumbled into the inferno. At the moment the spire falls, a collective gasp gives way to a wail that ripples through the crowd. Later news reports of the event show interviews with emotional Parisians fighting back tears as they describe the fire. French newspapers echoed this sentiment with one headline reading *"Notre-Dame Des Larmes"*, which translates to *Notre-Dame Tears*.

The French weren't all who mourned the loss of the 850 year old cathedral. The fire in France made global news. In the United States, images of the burning cathedral were shown on national and local news alike. For many days, even weeks, after the flames were extinguished, people around the world remained shaken by the event. World governments and wealthy individuals around the world donated to a fund to rebuild the cathedral. Within just a few weeks, over $100 million were donated to restore the cathedral to its former glory.

For many French citizens, Notre Dame was a representation of their national pride. For religious devotees around the world, the cathedral was a sacred structure, symbolizing the divine. It makes sense that French nationalists and devout Catholics the world over would feel some loss from this fire given its connection to their core beliefs. However, it makes almost no sense that I should have felt similar emotions watching the cathedral burn. As a secular American, the Notre Dame cathedral was neither a symbol of my nation nor a symbol of my religious faith. I may not have physically wept from the loss as many others did, but I did feel profound sadness in watching the videos of the burning church. Given the outpouring of donations and the unrelenting news coverage of the event, I was not alone with these emotions. It seems you did not have to be French or Catholic to feel emotionally pained by the destruction of the Notre Dame Cathedral.

These emotional responses to destruction transcend culture and have all the earmarks of a hardwired trait. We hate to see entropy consume order as it did on April 15th 2019. The human emotional response even looks to be proportional to the amount of order destroyed. Most would feel discomfort, but few would verbally castigate another for tearing a page from a book. A very different response would be elicited if the same person took a lighter from their pocket and set flame to the tome. *Homo sapiens* viscerally reviles destruction. In the same token, our species universally rejoices in the act of creation. We celebrate the birth of children. For thousands of years, we've celebrated each spring as new life again unfurls in the wake of winter's melt. We feel personal pride when we complete projects like knitted blankets, wooden chests, pieces of art, and other crafts. We beam with communal exhalation at the completion of complex creations that require cooperation. We take pride in building skyscrapers, running businesses, and manufacturing complex technology. These universal emotions are not a cultural phenomenon. This is something that occurs at the biological level. It's something evolution selected for.

Life on Earth would have been hard-pressed to flourish if each life form had to understand concepts like entropy and free energy to survive. As we've seen, cyno-bacteria didn't need to understand how it was impacting the universe's entropic increase. Prokaryotes didn't need to know that their metabolism was the predictable result of out-of-equilibrium processes with an abundance of free energy. In order to pass on their genes and survive, early life forms needed to *do* things that used free energy to create ordered gradients – they did not need to *know* how or why they did such things. This *doing* without *knowing* is what life on Earth radiated from. As long as life did the right things from an entropic perspective, it survived and passed on genes that code for more ordered gradients to flourish with available free energy. As far as evolution by natural selection at the multiverse level is concerned, cyanobacteria and *Homo sapiens* have a whole lot in common. We are both examples of biological carbon-based life that sprung up on planet Earth as a result of the abundant free energy reaching the surface of our planet from the sun. We even share a common ancestor that likely inhabited hydro-thermal ocean vents over 3.5 billion years ago. This ancient ancestor and all its evolutionary spawn would only survive if it was successful in using available free energy to create ordered gradients. Life on Earth never needed to know the exact figure for free energy change or entropy increase to survive. But as life became more complex, it needed to be able to feel these changes in order to flourish.

Our emotions are an evolutionary tool that allows us to intuit changes in entropy and free energy. To understand this, you probably need to reframe how you think about human emotions. Emotions like hunger, anger, sadness, joy, and lust all evolved as a way for us to quickly complete complex computations regarding survival probabilities, which in turn are based on entropy and free energy. It's not just humans that evolved these survival oriented emotions. Other animals have them, too.

Consider a primate living in Africa. This monkey is hungry. This feeling of hunger is the output of a calculation the monkey's physiology subconsciously completes when it needs more free energy in the form of carbon bonds found in the glucose of bananas. The monkey doesn't consciously think to itself "hmm, for the cells in my body to complete the required number of Krebs cycles, I'll need to obtain at least 42 grams of glucose today". Nope. The monkey just feels hunger which prompts it to go look for bananas. That's much more evolutionarily expedient.

Let's say this same monkey finds a tree with a bunch of ripe bananas growing on it. But alas, a sleeping lion lays in the shade of another tree only a few feet away. Upon seeing the lion, the monkey feels a rush of fear. In this case, fear evolved as a mechanism to quickly alert the monkey to things that pose a threat to its ability to pass on its genes. Monkeys that didn't evolve to fear lions didn't survive long to pass on this fearless gene. Now this monkey must perform another quick computation. Which emotion will win– fear or hunger? How badly does its body need food? The monkey's body does another quick free energy computation here, weighing the risk of death by starvation vs. the risk of death by the lion. It's been four days since this monkey last ate a banana, it's not wounded or hurt in any way, and it has a family of hungry monkeys waiting for it. Suddenly a rush of bravery courses through the monkey as it begins to tip-toe towards the banana tree. The subconscious computation decided that hunger wins over fear. The monkey's emotions of hunger, fear, and bravery are all results of subconscious survival computations which, at their core, are based on principles of thermodynamics.

Human emotions may be more nuanced than the emotions of a monkey looking for bananas, but they serve the same purpose. Our emotions are homologous to the emotions found in other animals, having evolved directly from these basic survival instincts. The core of these instincts has shepherded all life to stay away from highly entropic, destructive forces and to relish in bounties of free energy. This is true from cyanobacteria to *Homo sapiens*. We feel lust when our body does a computation that subconsciously says "That person displays phenotypes associated with genetics that have a high likelihood of survival and show minimal mutations in their genetic code caused by the increase of entropy." Try that one on your crush next time you're feeling lustful. Even feelings of love, regret, loneliness, envy, and trust are all results of this subliminal biochemical survival computation of our bodies.

The fact that these computations are rooted in terms of entropy and free energy can help explain our emotions. It can explain why I felt so stricken by the sight of an ancient burning cathedral and why I feel negative emotions in seeing anything destroyed. It can explain why we associate such positive emotions with the creation of ordered gradients. These universal emotional responses to destruction and creation are our entropic intuitions and they are a direct result of evolution by natural selection.

Religion

Throughout human history, our entropic intuitions have permeated several aspects of our culture – most notably, religion. For example, many world religions share the common concepts of heaven and hell. In Islam, Jannah is the "paradise garden" and Jahannam is where the souls of evildoers go for eternal suffering. Hinduism, Buddhism, the Sikh Religion, and even many ancient tribal religions share these concepts of heaven and hell. Notions of heaven and hell are so conserved across cultures through history that archeologists David Lewis-Williams and David Pearce argue in their 2005 book, *Inside the Neolithic Mind*, that there must be a neuroscientific explanation for the overwhelming similarities.

While depictions of heaven differ across cultures, all accounts of heaven share a strong common thread. The thread that ties all these divine lands together is the bond of free energy. Heaven is depicted as a place where there is no increase in entropy[26].

Heaven is the place where our youthful eternal souls reside. There is no sickness. The gardens of heaven bear eternal fruit. There is no war, no fighting, no death, no rot, no decay, and no aging. In heaven, there is enough free energy to make all ordered gradients eternal, including our human souls. Heaven must be powered by an infinite source of free energy; a truly divine dream shared by every biological organism on Earth.

Conversely, hell is depicted as a place devoid of free energy and rife with entropic increase. Christian hell is depicted as a place of fire, brimstone, death, pain, and suffering. In the Quran, Jahannam is also called "the fire", "the blaze", and "That which Breaks into Pieces". In the Buddhist faith, there are many layers of hell or Narakas. One level of Buddhist hell called Tapana is *"where hell guards impale beings on a fiery spear until flames issue from their noses and mouths"*. No biological life which depends on an abundance of free energy could thrive in such highly entropic hells.

Our entropic intuitions have shaped our collective visage of God. Godly attributes also appear to be conserved across many

---

[26] In an open system, it's theoretically possible for entropy to increase rapidly in one part of the system, and virtually stay unchanging in another part of the system. This would only be possible with substantial free energy inputs (and exergy degradation) from another part of the system. When this free energy runs out from the other part of the system, rot and decay would creep through the pearly gates as entropy finally has its way across the entire system. A true eternal heaven is thermodynamically impossible. However, cosmically ephemeral heavens could conceivably persist for billions of years before entropy caught up.

monotheistic religions. The typical monotheist believes in a singular God that is all-knowing (omniscient), all-powerful (omnipotent), and present everywhere at the same time (omnipresent).

A god capable of these three feats, could only be powered by a deep well of nearly eternal free energy[27]. If God is the embodiment of free energy, then the devil is the personification of destruction and entropy. For many religions, God is the bringer of light (free energy from the sun), and the devil is the master of darkness (where there is no free energy) and fire (a highly destructive entropic event).

It's clear that at least some of our pan-religious morality is shaped by these deep intuitions about free energy and entropy. For example, industrious hard work is exalted as a virtue in many religious texts. Many of Jesus's teachings promote using our available free energy to create and steward; otherwise known as working hard. Religions like Judaism place a similar emphasis on

---

[27] In the multiverse, an omniscient, omnipotent, and omnipresent God can be thermodynamically conceived of. This God would need to have access to the free energy in multiple universes, and could only operate as a God in a subset of these universes that it controlled. For example, being omniscient is a data processing problem. To be truly all-knowing, God would have to be able to compute the probability of every single future and past occurrence in the universe with nearly 100% accuracy. In Universe One, this would require X bytes of computing power to achieve. Let's say God has access to all the free energy in Universe Two which has 7X bytes of computing power. God could use the free energy and computing power of Universe Two in order to operate as an omniscient God in Universe One. Similar thought experiments can be completed that would give a multiverse God omnipotent and omnipresent powers as well.

the virtue of hard work. Jain Buddhists are an extreme example of holding non-violence as a virtue. Some Jain adherents walk with a broom to sweep the ground in front of them before they walk. This is to avoid treading on any insects or other small life forms. Jain Buddhists believe deeply in the virtue of protecting and stewarding other life on Earth. Animal welfare is mentioned many times in the Quran in the Islamic faith. This can also be seen in the Hindu religion, which teaches practitioners of the faith to avoid eating the meat of other animals.

Our entropic intuitions have permeated every major world religion. Our gods as well as our devils show our reverence for free energy and how we collectively revile the increase in entropy. The new paradigm of the entropic philosophy can help us make sense of these commonalities conserved across time and human culture.

Philosophy

Empedocles, an Italian philosopher from the fifth century BCE, is one of the first philosophers who tried to use reason and logic to describe his entropic intuitions. Empedocles dealt primarily with metaphysics, the branch of philosophy dealing with basic questions of existence, being, and knowing. The ontology he came up with about 2,500 years ago classified the physical world into a four-part theory of roots: the four roots that all other matter was derived from being air, water, earth, and fire. In Empedocles's story of the universe, these four roots were controlled and moved by two opposing forces – Love and Strife.

Empedocles wrote and shared his philosophy in the form of poetry. The following is a translated verse[28] from his poem *On Nature*, where the concepts of Love and Strife are explored. The bolded emphasis was added by me.

Twofold is what I shall say: for at one time they [the elements] grew to be only one
Out of many, at another time again they separate to be many out of one.
And double is the birth of mortal things, double their death.
For the one [birth] is both born and destroyed by the coming together of all things,
While the other inversely, when they are separated, is nourished and flies apart.
And these [the elements] incessantly exchange their places continually,
Sometimes by Love all coming together into one,
Sometimes again each one carried off by the hatred of Strife.
Thus insofar as they have learned to grow as one out of many,
And inversely, the one separating again, they end up being many,
To that extent they become, and they do not have a steadfast lifetime;
But insofar as they incessantly exchange their places continually,
To that extent they always are, immobile in a circle.

Empedocles should maybe be hailed as the father of thermodynamics and not Nicolas Carnot who explained these same concepts over 2,300 years later with different terminology, definitions, but sadly no poetry. According to Empedocles, the universe is made up of four roots, or elements. These four roots are controlled by the agents of love and strife. That is, all the movement and interactions between these four elements are caused by love and strife. What's described in this passage of *On Nature*,

---

[28] 3. This translation was taken from the Stanford Encyclopedia of Philosophy

is love bringing the elements together in birth and biological life. Strife is what causes the elements to explode apart into pieces again.

Empedocles's four roots were too simplistic and have since been replaced by the periodic table of elements. However, his description of love and strife as the main movers of physical matter still holds up, at least in the way they're described in *On Nature*. Love is free energy, which brings matter together in statistically unlikely configurations, such as life. In the absence of free energy, strife prevails — tearing matter apart into much more statistically likely pieces. Strife is, of course, entropy. In the absence of empirical scientific evidence, Empedocles accurately described entropy and free energy over 2,500 years ago, using little more than observation and his entropic intuitions.

Flash forward to the present day and we can still see our entropic intuitions permeating how we think about the world around us — Most notably in environmental ethics. We already covered environmental ethics earlier, but it's worth briefly revisiting through the view of entropic intuitions. I opened the chapter on stewardship with a quote from Aldo Leopold *"A thing is right when it tends to preserve the integrity, stability and beauty of the biotic community. It is wrong when it tends otherwise."* The entirety *A Sand County Almanac*, where this quote was taken, is the embodiment of Leopold's entropic intuitions. Leopold says that the land and biota have value outside of serving an economic purpose. However, Leopold is unable to articulate exactly what this value is. The entire book is an appeal for us to *feel* his argument, to *feel* the same entropic intuitions about the environment that he does. The poetic descriptions of his farm in Wisconsin succeeded in helping others empathize with his entropic intuitions, even without quite understanding where these emotions were logically rooted. The movements of Deep Ecology and philosophical ecocentrism have their roots in Leopold's entropic intuitions.

Outside of environmental ethics, entropic intuitions shine through in the new global philosophy proposed by Yuval Harari. Harari calls his new philosophy, or story as he refers to it, Dataism.

According to Harari, all of our social, political, and economic structures can be viewed as data processing systems. "Dataism declares that the universe consists of data flows, and the value of any phenomenon or entity is determined by its contribution to data processing... We may interpret the entire human species as a single data processing system, with individual humans serving as its chips." Dataism, as propounded by Harari, is based on observation. Harari observed that we used to give authority to Gods when we were theists. When we were humanists, we gave authority to individual selves and our feelings. Dataism gives power to information and big data. What we observe today is a near reverence for big data and data flows. We have observed that humans are superior data processors compared to any other life on Earth. Data-ism is based on these observations. Big data is physically embodied as gradients of ones and zeros stored on a computer drive. Keeping this data intact, processing it, and gleaning relevant insights from it takes a lot of free energy inputs. Our love for big data is a predictable output of our evolutionary entropic intuitions.

...

Religion and philosophy aside, modernity is imbued with our collective cultural entropic intuitions. The Extinction Rebellion movement started in the United Kingdom in 2018 to rally the world together to stop climate change and ecological collapse. The anger and zeal that fuels this rebellion doesn't come from reading environmental ethics texts – it swells up organically inside us. Zero Waste and minimalism are two other modern movements that are picking up steam and can be traced back to our entropic intuitions. In western culture, we worship entrepreneurs and start-ups who can find new ways to use available free energy to create or steward ordered gradients. Evolution imbued us all with these entropic intuitions.

We humans have strong emotions tied to creation and destruction. These emotions came directly from the process of natural selection by evolution which selects for the propagation and survival of ordered gradients. While our emotions, our entropic intuitions, are a glimpse into the window of truth about our universe and our origins, we can't see everything through this window. Our view is limited by the evolutionary niche we came to fill.

The human mind is like a cabin in the middle of a forest. As long as we are human, we are trapped in this cabin and are not allowed to leave. At least this house we're trapped in gave us a window to look through and study the world. We can see from this window a few trees, and can even analyze the bark and leaves of a few trees in detail. From inside the house, it's tempting to think that the whole world is a forest and that all trees look like the ones outside our window. If we were able to step outside the house, we'd soon discover that the moral landscape is so much more diverse and varied than forests consisting of just a few types of trees. The complete moral landscape also consists of oceans, deserts, tundra, and swamps. Our entropic intuitions have let us see the forest through a window, but it has not emotionally prepared us for the moral landscapes that lie beyond.

The entropic philosophy flings open the door of the cabin we're trapped in and forces us to step outside and explore. Once we leave the house, we'll find that our entropic intuitions are limited and the free energy computations we perform are imperfect. Our emotional calculations were good enough for our original niche in the African savannah, but these computations are failings us now that we've left that niche. There's quite a lot we didn't evolve to know or perceive.

Up to this point, I've mostly presented us with arguments and examples that our entropic intuitions agree with. So far, Hume would say that this philosophy is just an extremely elaborate *post hoc* reasoning for what my own emotions already wanted me to think. This changes in the next section of the book. The ethical questions I dive into in the next section make me uncomfortable, and there are some conclusions that I disagree with at an emotional level.

As we apply the ethics of the entropic philosophy, we'll see that it cares little for what my emotions are. By definition, this philosophy comes from outside of our humanity and does not have humans at the center of morality. It is literally in-human.

Humanists will not like some of what's presented next. While what I've presented so far mostly agrees with our entropic intuitions, some of what we could see in the wider applications of this philosophy may not agree so well with our logically limited emotions, stuck back in an ancient niche we've since transcended.

In the next section, the moral imperatives of the entropic philosophy are applied to pressing philosophical questions. Next, we'll explore the real life applications of the entropic philosophy related to the environment, biotechnology advances, and artificial intelligence. We'll get a better understanding of how looking beyond our entropic intuitions can better help us understand the world around us, and even explain phenomena like the ubiquity of the modern patriarchy. The door of our cabin is unlocked now. Let's go explore and see what lies beyond the window.

Chapter Summary

- Our emotions are a complex computation about free energy and entropy that were honed over billions of years of evolution.

- We see these entropic intuitions playing out in our philosophies from Empedocles to Yuval Harari.

- Our entropic intuitions have also permeated our religions—most notably in how we conceive of heaven and hell.

- Our entropic intuitions are imperfect, and we humans have blind spots regarding the most efficient way to slow entropy's increase.

10

An Entropic Explanation for the Patriarchy

MY NAME IS Stevie Wiegel[29], but I don't know that it should be. I struggle with what to call myself – specifically what my last name should be. I've been married for almost six years now and haven't changed my last name yet. My husband's last name is Kaschke and mine is Wiegel. I call this the easiest activism I've ever participated in. It was easier to keep my name than to change it, but laziness isn't why I do it. I keep my name because of what changing it represents. To me, taking my husband's name represents a vestige of female ownership by men.

---

[29] I changed my name to Stevie Kaschke just before publishing the book. I left this section because it's an illustrative introduction to the topic of this chapter.

My husband understands my choice completely. He's even offered to take a new neutral last name with me[30] and has seriously considered taking my last name. Six years later, we're still trying to figure out what to do. In part, my husband is so understanding because like many men of his generation, he carries some guilt with him for what his ancestors have done to women. It's easy for the next generation to forget, but it's only been a few decades since women in the United States were barred from taking out lines of credit or owning property, and only a few hundred years since women were treated more like livestock than like humans. In many places outside the United States, these things aren't history, they're current events.

Women taking their husband's name is just one embodiment of the patriarchal culture we live in. The patriarchy is so ubiquitous and has been around so long, we hardly notice it anymore. Few, except academic anthropologists, even seriously question why we live in a patriarchy. But it's a question worth asking. Why do *Homo sapiens* live in a patriarchal society? To date, there appears to be no good biological or social reason to explain the ubiquity of male domination in human social structures. It's not because men are stronger than women or any other biological difference between men and women. It's not because men are smarter than women or better suited psychologically for leadership. These theories have all been pretty well debunked. And yet man, and not woman, has

---

[30] The current leading contender here is Diesel. How does Stevie and Ty Diesel sound? We think we'd need to buy some motorcycles and get half-sleeve tattoos, but we could pull that name off.

emerged the clear winner again and again in the post-agricultural world. Why?

Hints to this question can be found by looking to other animals and their social structures for answers. In the animal world, true matriarchies are rare[31], but not unheard of. A 2018 review of animal behavior in 76 species revealed that 10% of surveyed species were known to have predominantly female leaders (Jennifer E Smith, *Obstacles and opportunities for female leadership in mammalian societies: A comparative perspective*). While many species displayed some behaviors indicative of female leadership, only eight species emerged with a clear and repeated pattern of behavior that can be defined as a true matriarchy. This list includes animals such as orcas, elephants, lemurs, lions, hyenas, and bonobos. The behavior of these eight matriarchal animals has something to teach us about how female leaders rise to power. There are three specific behaviors or traits these matriarchs have in common that can help us provide an entropic explanation for the patriarchy.

The first trait is a long lifespan, resulting in multiple generations living together simultaneously. The leaders in many long-lived species are post-menopausal females. This is the case with elephants, orcas, and hyenas. Why should the older females lead and not the younger, faster, more powerful females of childbearing

---

[31] While rare, there does seem to be a large blind spot in our scientific knowledge around gender-egalitarian social structures in both animal and human behavioral studies. There seems to be a large emphasis on studying only the dichotomy of patriarchy (defined as predominantly male social leadership) and matriarchy (defined as predominantly female social leadership). More research on gender-egalitarian structures is needed.

age? The answer to this is simple; offspring. The females of child bearing age spend all their available free energy (in this case embodied as time, attention, and food calories) on rearing their children. The older, post-menopausal females no longer have children to tend to (or steward), so their free energy is now available for other intensive tasks such as leading hunts, navigating inter-group conflicts, and scouting new territories.

Other matriarchal species mitigate the stewardship burden of offspring in other ways. Lemurs do this in a direct way with paternal care, where the male lemurs are the primary caregivers to offspring. Lions in bonobos are highly cooperative caregivers where the cost of rearing offspring is spread over multiple different females and not just placed squarely on the individual mother. The result of both cases is the same; female free energy is diverted away from childcare and can now be spent on leadership activities.

Childcare isn't the only thing these species do differently. Another commonality between matriarchal species is matrilineal succession. In a matriline, status and leadership are passed down from mother to daughter, such that when the mother dies, the daughter will inherit her leadership role and resources. Elephants, orcas, hyenas, and lemurs all pass on their inheritance of free energy reserves to their daughters instead of their sons. For example, many leaders get access to food that they themselves did not have to hunt and kill. The second inheritance of free energy comes in the form of social and ecological knowledge that's passed from mother to daughter. Elder elephant matriarchs often serve as repositories of social and ecological knowledge. These survival benefits get passed down to the daughter and not the son.

All these different species of matriarchs use different behaviors to achieve the same thing. It appears that whichever species has the free energy advantage over the other will be the primary leader. Matriarchal species achieve a free energy advantage by giving trust funds of ecological and social free energy to their daughters via matrilineal succession and by minimizing the stewardship burden of offspring for the female leaders. Reducing the stewardship burden of offspring is achieved by leveraging paternal care, cooperative female care, or recognition of post-menopausal females as leaders. We humans could also implement these cultural changes but don't. To better understand why we don't do these things, we'll need to go back to the agricultural revolution.

Free Energy Advantage of the Agricultural Revolution

Turning our attention back to *Homo sapiens* now – It's unclear how hunter-gatherers lived. It's probable that in many tribes women were equal decision makers or leaders, but there is a lot of debate about this in the field of anthropology. We are equipped with many of the traits described in true matriarchal animal structures such as a long life span resulting in multiple generations, and highly cooperative offspring care. There are some documented examples of cultures that had gender-egalitarian structures with matrilineal succession, such as the traditional Native American Hopi culture. In traditional Hopi culture, there is no concept of a superior or dominant gender. Also in North America, the Haudenosaunee Iroquois are said to have a clan mother that held veto power over all the chiefs in the tribe. Other examples of proposed historical matriarchies are thought to have existed in parts of India, China, and Vietnam.

If gender-egalitarian cultures or even true matriarchies existed, then how did the patriarchy come to permeate every corner of modernity? While we don't know exactly how our hunter-gatherer ancestors lived, we do have better historical records after the agricultural revolution. I believe the mystery of the ubiquitous patriarchy can be solved by examining the social effects of farming and its cascading results over the following 10,000 years. Men reaped the entire free energy harvest of the agricultural revolution. Yes, women ate the food as well, but men were the ones who gained the free energy advantage. This free energy advantage bestowed on men is what made the post-agricultural patriarchy grow like an invasive weed all over the world.

To understand what I mean by free energy advantage, we need to briefly revisit a principle of evolution by natural selection. Evolution does not endow any creature with more than the minimum of what it needs to survive and pass on its genes. The body morphology, sleep patterns, and bioenergetic requirements of *Homo sapiens*, like any other species on earth, were honed carefully over millions of years to fit exactly within the niche we originally occupied. Evolution by natural selection carefully sculpted *Homo sapiens* for hunting and gathering in the African Savanna. Our height and weight are a direct result of the survival needed to see beyond tall grasses and to be strong enough to hunt large mammals. Only those with high stamina passed on their genes as they excelled at endurance hunting and the grueling demands of life as a nomadic mother. The amount of free energy we required to sustain ourselves, and ultimately the amount of free energy we embody and wield personally, was entirely determined by this ecological niche.

About 10,000 years ago, human behavior and culture started transforming at a pace that far surpassed our biological evolution. Our minds and bodies stayed the same, mostly adapted for life in the savannah, but everything else about us changed. Biological evolution was left in the dust as human culture began its sprint towards some yet undefined destination. Nearly overnight, from an evolutionary perspective, our niche and resulting free energy requirements completely changed. This adoption of agriculture was completely responsible for our cultural change. Spears and bows were left in favor of tills and plows. Our nomadic way of life abruptly idled as permanent encampments grew alongside our new crops. Agriculture changed how we got our food and changed the entire course of human history.

This cultural innovation of agriculture obviated the need for spending days or even weeks on end hunting for food. Food became much easier to find. As we began to domesticate animals and keep them as livestock, we only needed to look a few paces out our door to find the next meal. Cultivating a field and reaping the harvest was hard work for our ancestors, but it wasn't as time or energy intensive as hunting and gathering to meet our caloric requirements.

The free energy reward that grew out of the agricultural revolution was not distributed equally between the genders. Man was shaped by evolution to hunt and collect food for the tribe. Woman was shaped by evolution with the predominant task to care for children. The agricultural revolution was the innovation that freed man from our original evolutionary niche. Many men, especially those that amassed wealth and power, were able to spend their days on anything that struck their fancy. Males were no longer free energy slaves to their original ecological niche of hunting.

The agricultural revolution did not liberate women from the roles of their original ecological niche the same way. Agriculture changed how we got our food but did very little to change the time and energy requirements needed to rear offspring. Women were still stuck spending all of the free energy evolution endowed us with on rearing children. The free energy gap between men and women only grew as males began to gain a stronger foothold as the gender with the free energy advantage.

While hunting got easier for males, child-rearing got more time-intensive for an individual woman after the advent of agriculture. Much like our closest genetic ancestor, the bonobo, *Homo sapiens* were thought to be highly cooperative caregivers. Hunter-gatherers didn't have nuclear families with one man, one woman, and a group of offspring directly cared for by one set of parents. Instead, females likely bore offspring from multiple men in the tribe and care was more communal through the group. For this reason, food, resources, and offspring care were dispersed among members of the group. Women and elders across the tribe pitched in to provide care for all the children in the tribe. Agriculture ended this communal way of childcare. The once communal childcare structure got divided up into households. Instead of having the resources of all the women in the tribe, resources for childcare were now mostly limited to the women in the home. This placed a higher free energy demand on individual women to care for their offspring.

This change was catalyzed by a new and radical idea that man can own land. It wasn't just farmland that got divided up into parcels; families got cleaved into neat little packages as well. In order to defend their property claim, males needed to stay close to their land. This spit up the tribe, which caused males to adopt a new mating strategy. The concept of female ownership by man was a direct result of the agricultural revolution and the invention of land ownership. Men used their newfound free time and free energy to defend their claims on their property and their mate.

The result was a growing disparity in free energy access between the genders. Males had an abundance of leftover free energy beyond maintaining homeostasis that was liberated when they no longer needed to spend all their free time hunting. Conversely, female free energy demands rose as even more time and attention were spent on child-rearing without the help and support of the tribe. These initial conditions of unequal free energy access spurred the divide of free energy to grow wider and wider with time.

The Widening Free Energy Gender Gap

After a few thousand years of agriculture and land ownership, males had firmly established their role as the gender with the free energy advantage. They had reclaimed the free energy of their physiology as they became liberated from their ecological niche of hunters. Shortly after this, males claimed ownership of the free energy encased in their property, domesticated animals, and the free energy of their female mates.

Men used their free energy advantage to further subjugate women. If a woman had free energy left over from offspring care, they were expected to use it on stewardship activities. With agriculture came permanent dwellings, and with permanent dwellings came the influx of human artifacts and owned objects. Women became the stewardship gender. Females were expected to spend all of their available free energy on childcare, cooking, cleaning, and mending. This continued to spur the cycle of liberated male free energy as women were subjugated as property and forced into stewardship roles. Males continued to gain access to more and more free energy, while women lost what little endowment of extra-physiological free energy we had in our historical hunter-gatherer niche.

Males used their free energy advantage to exploit and control more and more reservoirs of free energy on Earth. Men secured the benefits of the agricultural revolution and also came to control the free energy from the industrial revolution. At the onset of the industrial revolution, men owned the forests, the land, and the fossil fuels. Men used these free energy reservoirs to power their inventions, start new companies, and continue to shape their world in the male image.

Whether conscious or not, there's no doubt the collective patriarchy recognized its free energy advantage and where it came from. Males used their free energy advantage to create social structures, religions, governments, and laws that ensured women would remain subjugated stewards. We don't even need to look at history books to see this truth. There are hold-out cultures in the world today that still view women as property. The laws and religions made by the patriarchy are what continue to keep the status quo in these cultures. Men created the governments and the laws that ensured only their gender would have property rights to the free energy incased in the land and the human labor of business enterprises. These laws are still in effect today in over half the countries on Earth. Yes, in more than half the countries on Earth, women are still barred by law from land and business ownership.

Measuring Today's Free Energy Gap

Just barely enough time has passed in developed western countries for current generations to forget the recent past. It wasn't until the late 19th century that women were granted limited rights for property ownership. It took until the 20th century for women to gain the right to vote. It took until the 1970s for women to gain access to lines of credit that allowed them to start their own businesses. These incremental liberations of female free energy came too late for women to stake a meaningful claim in the free energy land grab of the technological revolution that occurred in the 1990s.

While legal and financial barriers have finally been lifted for women, other barriers to free energy access still persist even in the developed world today; the most notable are cultural and religious barriers. Today in the United States, almost 80% of the population identifies as having some religious affiliation. Nearly all of those in the US that are religious, identify as Christian, with other religions being the vast minority. The sacred text of Christianity leaves little to the imagination regarding what it thinks gender roles should be. Throughout the bible, we can find texts that sanctify and encourage the subjugation of women by men.

Christianity is a religion mired in post-agricultural patriarchy. Eve, not Adam, was the original sinner. Over 95% of the names in the bible are names of males. The Christian God has male pronouns and attributes. It was God's son, not daughter, that was sent to Earth. Jesus's disciples were exclusively male. In the Catholic church today, women are not allowed to hold positions of leadership in the church.

Religion shackles one arm of the modern woman, and a deeply ingrained patriarchal culture is the shackle on the other wrist. While there is no law codifying patrilinear succession in developed countries, modern culture ensures that men are the primary beneficiaries of free energy inheritances. For millennia of generations, sons inherited land, wealth, enterprise, and knowledge from their fathers. The historical momentum behind this cultural norm is slowing, but still strong. Even in today's modern culture, it would be strange for a woman with brothers to be the primary heir of her father's business or estate.

It's religion and culture that keep women to this day stuck on lower rungs of the hierarchy of free energy use. Only a small fraction of women in the devolved world have grown up in a truly liberated environment that allows them to use their free energy for creation. Today, fewer than 6% of CEOs at fortune 500 companies are women. The same is true for government positions. Only 19% of seats in the House of Representatives are filled by women.

Slightly better, but similar percentages show up in fields like science, engineering, and philosophy. Stepping outside the United States and taking a global perspective, these numbers plummet even further.

Liberating Female Free Energy

For many women today who've been able to free themselves from traditional stewardship activities like cleaning, cooking, and childcare– one final stewardship trap remains. Even in households that employ babysitters, maids, and use food preparation services, there is still one female stewardship task our culture imposes on women but not men; excessive personal grooming. There is strong cultural pressure for women to spend more time, attention, and money on their appearance than men (i.e. more personal free energy)

According to a 2014 survey of over 2,200 women, the average US woman spends 55 minutes every day on hair and makeup. This doesn't include time spent watching beauty tutorials, reading beauty reviews, trips to the salon, or time spent shopping for beauty related supplies. This is a significant burden both on a woman's time and money. My own calculations align with another survey showing the average US woman spends almost $4,000 a year on beauty related products and services. Over an adult lifetime, that's $250,000 a woman spends, that man doesn't have the cultural obligation to.

The gendered free energy stewardship tax extends beyond hair, makeup and skincare; women also face cultural pressure to own more clothing and adornments than men. Data from other surveys back this up and show that women go shopping more than men, own more clothing than men, and on average own twice as many pairs of shoes as men. Studies and surveys are nice, but even without them we can see it blatantly spread across modern western culture. Step into any clothing store that makes both men's and women's clothing. I'd estimated that the typical Zara location is split 75:25 between men's and women's clothing. You can physically see this at other stores like Target, H&M, Express, Banana Republic. Women are expected to buy and own more clothing and adornments than men. As we've already discussed in the chapter on stewardship, this further saps a woman's available time, money, and general free energy reserves.

Great strides have been made in recent history to liberate female free energy. In countries like the US, women can now inherit and own extrasomatic free energy in the form of land and enterprise. Nearly half the countries on Earth now recognize this right for women. Within those countries, some women have been liberated from their traditional stewardship tasks. In many households, males now at least partially participate in childcare, cooking, and cleaning. In other households, help is hired for these tasks. A subset of these women reject the modern cultural norms of hyper-grooming and hyper adornment. These women, albeit a small percentage of the world's population, have been fully liberated (see Figure 10.1). However, we need to keep a global perspective and remember that this is only a very small percentage of women in the world.

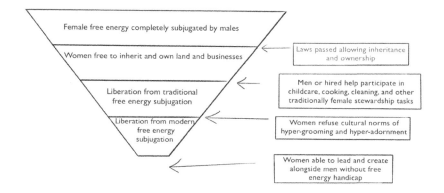

Figure 10.1 The funnel of female free energy liberation. Only a small subset of the world's population has made it all the way through this funnel.

As women filter through this free energy liberation funnel, the oppression and free energy subjugation become less and less severe. I was torn about even including the section describing the cultural challenges of hyper grooming and adornment because it seems so trivial compared to problems faced by women who are stuck further back in the funnel. I think it's important that women who make it further down the funnel use their newfound free energy agency to help those that have yet to be liberated. Less of our energy is needed fighting against the cultural norm of spending too much time and money on makeup and more attention is needed to help the estimated 35 million women who are trafficked or enslaved today. Feminist Mikki Kendall makes a similar point in her 2020 book *Hood Feminism*, and I couldn't agree more.

To clarify something that may be easily confused in this chapter, there is nothing morally wrong with choosing to spend your available free energy stewarding instead of creating. The entropic philosophy has defined both stewardship and creation as moral imperatives. A stay at home mother (or father) partakes in very important stewardship activities and it's just as morally important as business owners, engineers, and artists who spend their time creating. The point of this chapter isn't to advocate that every woman should be a creator of some sort. The point I'm trying to make is that every woman ought to have the choice and not be stuck stewarding if that's not what she wants. The main point of this chapter is that a woman or man ought to have the right to choose how they spend their free energy. At this point in world history, very few women have been afforded this basic right. Having women creators and leaders in our society will help us create and preserve diversity. This diversity of creations in turn helps slow the increase of entropy in the universe. It isn't just a personal sentiment of mine that women should have the opportunity to be leaders and creators. There's a logical backing behind it in the entropic philosophy.

...

The first step in fixing any problem isn't coming up with solutions. The first step is to fully understand the problem. In this chapter, I showed how concepts of entropy and free energy can help us understand how the patriarchy arose, and how it stays in place. The agricultural revolution provided a set of initial conditions that allowed men to gain a strong free energy advantage over women for a brief blip in human history. This initial advantage grew substantially over time.

This is an explanation, but it's not a solution. I'm not sure how exactly we get back to a gender-egalitarian culture, but I know that we can. Our species has existed for about 300,000 years. Only the last 10,000 of that has been spent in the post-agricultural patriarchy. We've already spent 96% of our collective time on Earth living as hunter-gatherer tribes that were very likely gender-egalitarian. We can get there again. This is not a call for a matriarchy or reparations for the last 10,000 years of female subjection by males. This is an appeal for us to truly embrace diversity. Together, both genders can help our species better achieve the goals laid out in the entropic philosophy.

This chapter illustrates one example of how using this new entropic paradigm can help us explain the world around us better. The entropic philosophy can help us make sense of our current world, and it can also help us shape our future. In the next chapter, we'll discuss how the entropic philosophy could be applied to help answer pressing ethical questions; many of which currently have no good answer.

Chapter Summary

- There are many examples of matriarchies in the animal world and ample anthropological evidence of gender-egalitarian hunter-gatherer tribes. Today, there's no accepted answer for why we live in a global patriarchy.

- In this chapter, I propose that the global post-agricultural patriarchy can be explained using the paradigm of the entropic philosophy.

- The reason men were able to completely subjugate women is because of a disparity of available free energy between the genders that started after the agricultural revolution and only compounded with time.

- If women wish to create alongside men, there are many layers of free energy that need to be liberated including:
  o Allowing women the right to own land and enterprise
  o Freeing women from stewardship burdens she doesn't wish imposed on her
  o Normalizing a woman's choice to refuse hyper-grooming and hyper-adornment

11

Entropic Ethics

IN 1751 THREE YEAR old Jeremy Bentham was found in his father's study reading a dense three-part tome on the history of England. No one was surprised that the intellectual child prodigy grew into a highly educated lawyer and philosopher. Bentham is maybe best known for his philosophical theory of utilitarianism. The ethical concept of utilitarianism is introduced in every intro to philosophy course using a thought experiment called the trolley problem.

Imagine you're about to cross the train tracks when you hear a trolley barreling down the tracks to your left. You pause waiting for it to pass until you notice something disturbing. Five people are tied to the tracks to your right. A flash of relief washes over you as you realize that right at the intersection where you stand is a lever that will put the trolley on an alternate set of tracks before reaching the five people tied up. You can pull the lever and save the five people. Relief gives way to horror as you realize there is still one person tied to the alternate set of tracks that the trolley will kill if you pull the lever. What do you do? Do you pull the lever to save the five and kill the one? Jeremy Bentham would have pulled the lever as he believed this was the most moral thing to do. Pulling the lever let the most people live, and killed the least. This choice gives the greatest good to the greatest number of people. Pulling the lever is the utilitarian thing to do.

Depending on a few key details, pulling the lever is also the hard-lined Entropian choice. Utilitarians strive to maximize happiness and well-being for the greatest number of people. Entropians are similar in that they seek to maximize for certain parameters – Entropians strive to maximize available free energy and gradients in the universe. In the following sections of this chapter, we'll explore what Entropic Ethics has to say about pressing questions in the fields of environmental ethics, bioethics, information ethics, and economic ethics. Each of these sections could easily be a chapter unto themselves and each answer to a single question could easily take up multiple pages. The following is just a cursory look at some pressing questions in a few subfields of ethics.

Environmental Ethics & Political Philosophy

Can and should man own property?

Historically, this question has been thought about in terms of political philosophy, not ethics. This question is not only an ethical question, it is a question of environmental ethics. By definition, property is derived somehow from the land – whether it is the land itself or resources once taken from the land. Property is a function of the land and our interaction with it, making the question of natural rights and property ownership –at least in part—a question of environmental ethics.

John Locke is maybe the most well-known political philosopher to ever muse on the question of property and natural rights. According to Locke, *Homo sapiens* is the only species that possess "unalienable" natural rights. These natural rights include the right to "life, liberty, and property"[32]. Locke's logic behind his theory of natural rights is rejected by most secular philosophers. This is because Locke says that it's God that gave us these special rights that other species of animals don't have. Without a God to endow us with these special rights, Locke's theory crumples.

There's another problem with Locke's theory of natural rights and property ownership. Locke argued that man can come to own a parcel of land and its natural resources by a process of "labor mixing". This is how the earliest humans to settle a parcel of land came to "own" it. Maybe a family of settlers comes across a parcel of unsettled and wild land. They mix their labor (personal free energy) with the land to make a farm and homestead. Locke would say that by mixing their personal free energy (which that individual owns and has a right to) with that of the land, those settlers have now come to own that land as their property. To make this even

---

[32] It was Jefferson that switched out the term "property" for the "pursuit of happiness" in The Declaration of Independence.

more clear, think of a tribal human living 5,000 years ago who wanted to make a flute. This human would go to the forest, and take a sizable limb from a tree. This limb would then be hollowed out with holes added to it (the free energy input) which then transfigured the limb of the tree into human property—the flute. In essence, Locke is saying that by mixing something owned (the free energy of our labor) with something unowned (natural resources), that we then come to own these resources. I'm not alone in thinking that this is a pretty weak argument for property ownership. Below is an illustrative quote from Robert Nozick's book *Anarchy, State and Utopia*.

"Why isn't mixing what I own with what I don't own a way of losing what I own rather than a way of gaining what I don't? If I own a can of tomato juice and spill it in the sea so that its molecules (made radioactive, so I can check this) mingle evenly throughout the sea, do I thereby come to own the sea, or have I foolishly dissipated my tomato juice?"

If we use the paradigm of the entropic philosophy to probe the question of property ownership, we find no logical backing endowing us with rights to own property. Property is thought of as a possession that you can do with whatever you please. If you own a parcel of land you can clear cut all trees and kill any insects or small game that doesn't suit your fancy. If you own a TV, you can take a baseball bat to it and break the screen. Under the Lockean paradigm of property ownership, no one will stop you or say that wasn't within your rights.

However, an Entropian would say that it's not within our rights as conscious agents to waste available free energy in a way that promotes a more efficient increase of entropy. Breaking a TV for fun or clear-cutting all the trees on a piece of property are two examples of things that increase the rate of entropic increase instead of slowing it down. On a larger scale, examples could include blowing up planets, breaking up asteroids, or degrading other large-scale cosmic gradients. If we don't have a right to do with things as we please, do we have a right to them at all?

According to the entropic philosophy, we don't have a right to property ownership in the traditional sense. However, we do have a right, a moral obligation even, to property stewardship. We have no right to own property and do with it as we please, but we do have the right, the responsibility even, to steward free energy (of which all property is a form of) in a way that most efficiently slows the increase of entropy in our universe. This stewardship principle applies to all the natural resources we have access to in our cosmic endowment, as well as here on Earth.

Describing the social and legal structure of a stewardship-based paradigm of property ownership is outside the scope of this section. Suffice to say that cultural and legal changes would certainly need to be made. The only thing I'll say on this note is that an ideal stewardship structure would optimize how we use available free energy to slow the increase of entropy given our physical and cognitive abilities. It does not seem that our current structure of property ownership in any way optimizes for this outcome.

Bioethics

Should we develop technologies that could result in biological inequalities?

If you visited the island of Flores in Indonesia 55,000 years ago, you may have had a very odd welcome. Along with Komodo dragons, this island was home to species of pygmy humans known as *Homo floresiensis*. *Homo floresiensis* certainly had human features, but was visibly different from *Homo sapiens*, especially regarding their height. Many of this species of hominid didn't grow taller than four feet. *Homo floresiensis* wasn't the only other species of hominid around recently. Anthropologists now know that at least four species of humans co-existed on Earth: *Homo sapiens*, Neanderthals, *Homo Erectus*, and *Homo floresiensis*. It wasn't until about 40,000 years ago with the extinction of the last Neanderthals that *Homo sapiens* found ourselves alone.

We've gotten used to being the only child. It now seems strange to think of other species of humans living among us. Some of us still regrettably seem to have a hard time living and thriving with other races of our species. Our brief days as an only child may be again coming to a close. In the near future, it seems probable that we could speciate – leaving us with a new sibling to share the Earth with.

Advances in genetic engineering, biotechnology, and medical technologies are what could drive this new speciation event. Yuval Harari's book *Homo deus* describes what he believes could be the next species of deity-like hominid. Using genetic engineering, there is the potential to radically alter our minds and bodies. We could make a new species that is bigger, stronger, healthier, and vastly more intelligent. Harari, along with many other futurists, speculates that these technologies will not be available to all of us. Only the wealthiest among us will have access to these biological upgrades.

Should we try to stop such a speciation event from happening? Previously, the rich could buy lavish homes, luxury cars, and eat decadent exotic foods, but they did so with the same minds and bodies as the rest of us. In the near future, money could buy more than private islands and trips to outer space. Money could buy near immorality and a mind that would seem god-like to us today. If we can't all have these upgrades all at once, should any of us have access to biological upgrades at all? If we look to the paradigm of the entropic philosophy for an answer, we will find one that many will probably be very unsatisfied with. 100,000 years ago four species of hominid co-existed on Earth—their differences guided by evolution by natural selection to make sure each was adapted for their niche of available free energy. These different niches of free energy create the biodiversity we see on Earth today. As we covered in chapter seven, diversity is more than an efficient tool for using free energy, it also doubles as a safety net against catastrophe.

It's not diversity that we seem to have a problem with. We're able to embrace the innate diversity within our species until it reaches a tipping point. We celebrate diversity of skin color and diversity of culture. We welcome and respect diversity in beauty, athletic ability, and even intelligence within our species. We all recognize that others may be born with better or worse genetics, or into wealthy or poor families. No one today is calling for all humans to have exactly the same genetics to make us equal. Similarly, very few are calling for all humans to have exactly the same numbers in our bank accounts to make us equal. We love diversity until it tips too far into the realm of inequality.

Evolution by natural selection does not share in our disdain for inequality. If anything, natural selection seems to thrive on inequalities. Evolution finds these small differences and amplifies them over time until the end result is no longer recognizable from the starting inputs. Most already celebrate the biodiversity on our planet. The ethics of the entropic philosophy indicate that we should also celebrate biological diversity in humans – no matter how diverse these differences get.

Information Ethics

What goals should we give an artificial super intelligent agent?

Writing this book makes me feel like a dog trying to walk on its hind legs. If there's anything writing this book has taught me, it's that humans are not particularly efficient at activities that take long-term concentration, assimilation of information, and paying close attention to small details. I get distracted and have pesky biological needs like eating, sleeping, and maintaining mental health. I get writer's blocks, feel discouraged, and sometimes just feel like lazing around. Computer algorithms don't have these same problems.

Just 15 years ago the general public was still skeptical about artificial intelligence and its ability to impact our lives anytime soon. Now you'd be hard-pressed to find anyone living in a developed country whose life hasn't been impacted by this technology. Siri, Alexa, Amazon, Spotify, Tesla, and Nest are all examples of consumer technologies that utilize artificial intelligence algorithms in their products. These are just examples of highly visible consumer goods. Behind the scenes, AI is also transforming our lives in healthcare, manufacturing, research, and enterprise.

We've collectively accepted AI into our daily lives, and many now see how an artificial super intelligent agent could arise in the near future. By definition, a superintelligence would be vastly smarter than us humans. The difference between us and a superintelligence would not be similar to the difference between the village idiot and Einstein. The intelligence gap between us and a superintelligence will likely be closer to the gap between us and a hamster. We as humans think we're special – that something in our human nature can never be replicated; that we are the pinnacle of intelligence on the planet. That may be true for now, but we need to realize that our intelligence is not special. Instead of viewing ourselves as the smartest on the planet, *we need to start viewing ourselves as the least intelligent organism that could occupy our niche*. We are the minimum viable solution created by evolution to hunt large mammals on the African Savanna. As our niche expands on this planet and beyond, our intelligence does seem to be a dangerous limiting factor.

We may be on the verge of an intelligence explosion resulting in the creation of a super-intelligent agent that makes us look like a colony of hamsters. What goals should we try to imbue this agent with? Other philosophers and researchers have thought at length about this question. Eliezer Yudkowsky proposes that we should give a seed AI the goal of helping realize humanity's "Coherent Extrapolation Volition" or CEV. Yudkowsky describes his idea of CEV as follows:

"Our coherent extrapolation volition is our wish if we knew more, thought faster, were more the people we wished we were, had grown up farther together; where the extrapolation converges rather than diverges, where our wishes cohere than interfere."

In other words, our CEV is what the collective ideal version of humanity may wish to have happen in the future. I find the idea of using humanity's CEV as a goal for a super-intelligent AI extremely lacking. Using the hamster analogy, why use the collective thoughts of hamsters to define the goal of a superintelligence that can affect change throughout the cosmos? The hamsters may tell the AI that their ideal wishes are to use all the free energy in the universe to create more hamsters, hamster habitat, and to make sure there are plenty of hamster wheels around to play on.

This has two main problems: The first is that maybe the hamsters don't know what's best for their collective wellbeing and happiness. This is so even if the hamsters "thought faster" or had "grown up farther together". Hamsters don't understand themselves very well and may collectively wish for things that are either harmful to them or keep them from feeling fulfillment or happiness. A super-intelligent agent may know better than the hamsters what their ideal collective state would be. The agent would know better than to grant the hamsters' CEV wish of infinite hamster wheels, knowing that there is a better way to maximize collective hamster wellbeing.

The second problem with using CEV as a goal is that maybe the power and resources of a super-intelligent agent could be spent on activities of higher value than serving hamster masters. I propose in this book that there are goals and morality in the universe that go beyond what we think, feel, and want as humans. Using CEV as the goal for superintelligence flies in the face of this proposal. We would only use CEV as the ultimate goal if we thought that there was no morality or greater goal beyond what we humans currently think and feel.

Nick Bostrom points out in his book, *Superintelligence: Paths, Dangers, and Strategies* that a super-intelligent agent would have access to our cosmic endowment of free energy. As a brief recap, a super-intelligent agent could use Dyson Spheres and self-replicating von Neumann Probes to capture and use all the free energy possible in our corner of the universe. Should we spend our cosmic endowment of free energy on the equivalent of hamster wheels and more hamsters? If you ask the hamsters, they would say this is a great idea.

We as humans can only see and perceive what evolution by natural selection says that we needed to see and perceive to survive and pass on our genes. This limitation in our senses and intellect almost certainly stops us from knowing the true nature of the universe and the world we live in. In his 2019 book *The Case Against Reality: Why Evolution Hid the Truth from Our Eyes,*

Donald Hoffman argues that evolution favors fitness over reality; that our reality is based on our ability to have kids, not about the truth of the universe around us. Our view of reality is limited at best, and flat out wrong at worst. Using humanity's CEV just makes no sense when you begin to see us for what we really are; small, insignificant, possessing relatively low intelligence compared to what is possible, and completely ignorant of reality.

A superintelligence has the potential to carry out the moral objectives of the entropic philosophy far better than a human mind could. Goals such as human happiness or human wellbeing are very hard to define, let alone quantify. Much to the delight of an algorithm, entropy and free energy can be defined using equations. Using the ethics of the entropic philosophy, the goal given to a seed AI could be to "Maximize efficiency in slowing the increase of entropy in the universe." This goal leaves our hamster-like minds unsatisfied, but it satisfies something much bigger than ourselves. It may not be possible yet for us to think like gods, but if we are going to start playing god with technologies like AI, we need to start thinking beyond our limited human experiences.

Economic Ethics
Is the Entropic Philosophy compatible with Capitalism?

As we've already discussed, the free market is a great tool for catering to human diversity and creating a diverse and abundant supply of physical goods. This part of the free market and capitalism is compatible with the moral imperatives of the entropic philosophy. In many ways, the free market is almost like an extension of evolution by natural selection. If there is an open niche of free energy available, the free market rewards an entrepreneur who discovers the niche and fills it. This phenomenon has been previously described in the 1960s by bio-economist Georgescu-Roegen who described economic processes as a continuation of biology in terms of entropy and free energy.

But the free market is entropically imperfect – it has blind spots. Specifically, the free market undersupplies public goods and results in what's called "the tragedy of the commons". The free market doesn't value clean air, biodiversity, or resource conservation for future generations. The free market isn't working towards any goal – it just puts out whatever humans say has value with their wants, desires, and emotions, at that specific point in history. Philosophically, the free market functions on a mix of hedonism and nihilism. Our current global operating system has no goal, no plan, and no real morals or ethics. Because of these blind spots, the free market falls short of a true entropic economic solution.

It's not just the free market that isn't fully compatible; the way corporations are set up is also problematic. To understand the problem, we need to take a deeper look at what a corporation is actually set up to do. The purpose of any for-profit corporation is not to produce goods or services; the purpose of a for-profit corporation is to provide value to its shareholders. In fact, that's the very definition of a corporation: An entity with a fiduciary duty to provide value to the shareholders. That means the purpose of IKEA or any other furniture company is not to make furniture. The purpose of IKEA is to provide value to its shareholders. The furniture is just a byproduct that gets made in the process of returning value to the shareholders of IKEA.

To better understand this definition, let's drill down into the terms a little more starting with the term value. As we just discussed above, value is money. Money is a fiat currency that serves as a placeholder for humans to trade free energy. And what is a shareholder? A shareholder is an individual human that owns a portion of the corporation. So the purpose of a corporation in entropic philosophy speak is to provide free energy to the individual humans that own it. There is nothing in that definition putting constraints on how the individual humans who own a corporation get their free energy returns or what they do with the free energy they receive. The result is what we so often see in today's corporations: waste production, environmental damage, wasteful use of resources, and natural habitat destruction. Corporate structures and incentives are part of what leads to the tragedy of the commons.

The economy of the developed world today isn't fully capitalistic. There are checks and balances from the government that make sure the blind spots of the free market are seen. Laws have been passed to make sure our air and water stay clean, that we protect some land and wildlife, and that we conserve some natural resources. It's outside the scope of this book to provide a solution to this problem. We can look to government, social and economic systems, and even rethink how we define money[33] in order to solve this problem. While I don't have a solution, I do have an answer to the question posed at the beginning of this section, and the answer is that pure capitalism is not fully compatible with the ethics of the entropic philosophy.

…

I opened this chapter with an anecdote about Jeremey Bentham, the father of utilitarianism. Some of Bentham's critics say that his thinking is too soulless and inhuman. They criticize Bentham for being too much of a systematic thinker and say that he lacked empathy and human nuance in his computational thought process. Many philosophers think that human morals should be more than just a computation resulting in the greatest good for the greatest number of people. Without a human touch, the entropic philosophy on its own is even more inhuman and soulless than Bentham's utilitarianism. At least utilitarianism cared for human wellbeing. Ultimately, the entropic philosophy does not care if we humans are happy or not. This is something that should bother us about the entropic philosophy.

Maybe the most important question we can ask ourselves now is how much of our humanity do we keep as we transcend our

---

[33] Redefining how we think about money could be one solution. We've been using fiat currency for our entire existence. What if we based our currency on the only thing that has real value to any life in the universe? What if we tied the value of an item to free energy/ exergy?

original niche and become trans-human? What emotion-based values do we discard or keep as our minds expand beyond their previous limits? We are not perfect entropy calculators. We are living, breathing, feeling, imperfect creatures. How do we balance the imperfect emotional nature of the human experience with the computational unfeeling ethics of the entropic philosophy? Neither myself nor Bentham has any answers to this question yet.

I asked a lot of questions in this chapter to illustrate how the ethics of the entropic philosophy apply to real-world problems we face today. In the next chapter, I tackle even bigger questions; questions humans have been asking since the dawn of our existence. In the next chapter, We'll dive into existential questions and the new answers provided by the entropic philosophy.

- We can use the ontology of the entropic philosophy to inform our ethics.

- *Q: Can and should man own property?* A: We don't have a right to own property that we can do anything with, but we can "own" what we choose to steward.

- *Q: Should we develop technologies that could result in biological inequalities?* A: The entropic philosophy teaches that we should create and steward diversity, including human diversity – even if that means a human speciation event.

- *Q: What goals should we give an artificial super intelligent agent?* A: We should give it the goal of preserving gradients to slow the increase of entropy.

- *Q: Is the entropic philosophy compatible with capitalism?* A: Not exactly. The free market driving pure capitalism has entropic blind spots and degrades many natural gradients. While capitalism seems to be a great tool for creating, it doesn't seem to be a good tool for stewarding.

- The entropic philosophy is calculated and mathematical. Humans are emotional and imperfect. How can we reconcile a purely logic-driven philosophy with our human existence?

12

Existential Answers

ABOUT HALFWAY THROUGH my master's degree in biotechnology, I had the untimely realization that I didn't want to be a corporate scientist or engineer. Characterizing proteins for a living didn't sound so fun anymore – especially not after discovering the start-up scene on campus. I made friends with student founders starting companies in med-tech, clean-tech, and consumer products. Before graduating, I had two failed startups of my own under my belt; a nanomaterials texturing company and a clean-tech microgrid company that didn't pan out. As it turns out, trying to start a company on a deadline with a group of students you just met is really hard to pull off.

I was jealous of my friends who had made it work and struggling with severe feelings of self-doubt but still had one trick up my sleeve to try. I took a job as a biomedical engineer at a friend's company but spent my free time on my own startup venture. My husband and I were outdoor enthusiasts with a few ideas for novel outdoor gear. We decided to start a company together, Xolo Outdoor, and got to work fabricating prototypes of our camping products.

We incorporated Xolo Outdoor and raised a small amount of investment money to help get it going. We made 40 prototypes of our new multi-tool invention and were granted a patent for it. In April of 2017, we launched our first product. I remember dancing around our apartment in a goofy display of joy and excitement when we got our first round of orders in. We advertised on social media and found ourselves selling more than we expected in the first few months.

It wasn't an instant success. We were lucky if we made 20 sales in a week, and that was certainly not enough to make a living on. Every penny we made went straight back into advertising, buying more inventory, and scaling. At this point, I'd been working on Xolo Outdoor for over a year and hadn't paid myself a penny. I was working at the medtech startup but was being paid mostly in company equity – with only a portion of my paycheck in the form of spendable cash. We were broke, struggling, and getting very discouraged as sales started declining a few months after launch.

This is the point in a start-up that you hear about in so many success stories. Entrepreneurs hit their financial and mental nadir, but still somehow muster the inner grit to push through to success. I was at this point – living off of 67 cent frozen burritos and dressing almost exclusively in thrift store clothes. The stress of near six-figure student loans pressing harder and harder on me. I was not in a good place as the self-doubt, financial stress, and burnout pressed me like a vice on all sides. I felt pinned and ready to implode.

Many founders reach the point I reached with Xolo, but the ones that made it were able to push through. The ones that made it all seem to possess an unwavering belief that what they're doing is right – that the world needs what they're making. My company didn't fail because of a bad product-market fit or because of some fatal mistake my husband and I made. My company failed because ultimately, I didn't believe in what we were doing. In many ways, I felt guilty about my company. I felt guilty about buying cheap plastic trinkets from China, marketing them up 600%, and advertising them on social media. It felt like my company added to our cultural problem of overconsumption and waste. It just didn't feel ethical or important to me.

These feelings and the eventual result of dissolving my company had a profound impact on me. My failed business precipitated a full-on existential crisis that had been a hair away from being triggered for years anyway. As my background existential angst turned into a raging crisis, the questions I always had became a key focus for me. The main question I couldn't shake was *"Why couldn't I be passionate about Xolo Outdoor?"*. This question was followed by many more: *What's morally wrong with consumerism? Why does climate change or environmental damage matter? Why does anything matter? Why does my life matter?* You can see how it can continue to spiral from there.

I turned to philosophy for answers, starting with the oldest philosophies and working my way up to present-day thinking. I familiarized myself with ancient philosophies like stoicism and epicureanism and read the highlights from the enlightenment era. Kant and Hegel didn't have the answers I was looking for, so I moved on to 20th century thinkers like Nietzsche, Sartre, Camus, and Kierkegaard. The existentialists let me down, too. I found their answers to my existential questions to be weak and wanting. The existentialist answers say that life only has the meaning you imbue it with. That you're your own god, and that any continued search for answers is absurd. Existentialists hold that there are no answers and so we ought to just content ourselves with the ultimate meaninglessness of our existence the best we can. You can see how this is an unsatisfying place to end my search.

I reject existentialism for two reasons: The first is that I don't think it's useful and the second reason is that I don't think it's accurate. As more and more humans reject ancient antiquated religions, we turn to philosophy to guide our morals and decisions. On an individual level, existentialism may be a passable tool for some to placate existential angst, but for many like me, it doesn't work at all. The human mind needs meaning, stories, and purpose. That's the very reason why religions are so ubiquitous across time and cultures. While existentialism may be marginally useful as an individual tool to alleviate existential suffering, I think it's useless at scale. Imagine a world full of seven billion nihilists, each believing themselves to be the god of their own universe. How can existentialism compel us to work together or find peace? How could our laws or legal system make sense if we all truly adopted this philosophy?

The second reason I reject existentialism is because I don't think it's accurate. There's a lot we didn't know about the world during the time of existentialist thinkers. We didn't know about DNA, the big bang, cosmic microwave radiation, or that we were capable of sending a man to the moon. We knew very little about ourselves and the universe we live in. We still don't know much, but we gain new insights and clues every day. Just because we didn't know enough in the late 1800s to divine answers, doesn't mean we'll never have any. I fundamentally disagree that the continued search for answers is meaningless or absurd. I think the notion that we'll never have answers is defeatist and shrouded in the ego of thinkers that didn't have the answers over 100 years ago.

Maybe the existential answers offered by the entropic philosophy are absurd, but the spirit of this philosophy is not. The essence of this philosophy is the humble and earnest search for answers and meaning using our ever growing pool of knowledge and understanding. I'm less sure about the validity of the answers outlined in this chapter, but very certain about the statement they make: that just because philosophers who lived 100 years ago didn't have answers, doesn't mean we never will. With that background, here are some long awaited answers to our existential questions.

Why are we here?

We're here as a result of evolution by natural selection playing out at the multiverse level. There would be selective pressure in the multiverse for traits that slow the increase of entropy. Biological life, humans included, is one example of a trait that can slow the increase of entropy. Biological life is like a savings account of free energy stored from our sun. We are here as a mechanism to help slow our universe down from reaching its eventual thermodynamic equilibrium.

What does it mean to be conscious?

Consciousness evolved as a mechanism that can be utilized by a physical system to gain access to free energy in the universe outside of the original niche in which it evolved. Physical systems that are not conscious cannot gain access to any free energy other than what is provided in the niche in which it evolved. To be conscious means to have the ability to gain access to free energy outside of an original evolutionary niche.

What does it mean to live a good and moral life?

You have lived a good and moral life if you have participated in slowing the increase of entropy in our universe. Just by being alive, you have achieved this. One can live an *exceptionally* moral life by participating in activities that slow the increase of entropy even more. An exceptional life is one filled with creation, stewardship, and conservation.

What should be the goal of humanity?

The goal of humanity should be to access the most free energy we can and use it to create ordered gradients. To achieve this, humanity will need to colonize our solar system, galaxy, and potentially our entire universe – physical laws permitting.

Entropia

I briefly asked you to think about a world filled with nothing but nihilists and how that could play out, but what would a world filled with Entropians look like? Would it be a utopia? As long as the second law of thermodynamics holds up, there can be no true utopia for us to take shelter in. The creeping tendrils of entropy will eventually permeate any utopian hold out and spread its suffering to all life, which entropy so despises. We cannot reconcile the existence of a utopia with the second law of thermodynamics. Given that entropy will only continue to increase, the best we can hope for is an Entropia.

From an entropic perspective, we are living in the dark ages – a dystopia of disorder. Our lives are pitifully short and punctuated by intense periods of individual and collective suffering. We accept this as the way life is and many can hardly imagine an alternative– so we hope for heaven in the afterlife instead. We accept war, cancer, mass extinction, poverty, and sickness as a fact of life and few of us hope for anything better. Until very recently, we could see no other option but to live with such pervasive suffering. It wasn't until sometime in the last 50 years or so that humanity could start to see visions for a different sort of life – One where we could apply salves of free energy to heal the wounds inflicted by entropy's relentless procession. We are just now gaining the knowledge and free energy access required to mount a meaningful resistance against our suffering.

The only entropic antidote is free energy – And even then, the antidote is temporary. Entropy will always win in the end as the arrow of time flies true towards the death of our universe. The good news for us is that this temporary relief from entropy's tyranny over life could last billions of years, and maybe longer. Knowledge and free energy can provide a lasting moratorium for life's suffering. Imagine a future where humanity has colonized our galaxy and has access to the free energy in some 250 billion stars. With the proper knowledge of ourselves and our physiology, there's no reason why the average human couldn't live for thousands or even millions of years with relatively minimal illness or physical suffering.

Now imagine this civilization as an Entropian society. In an Entropia, there would be no war or destructive infighting. Peace and cooperation would have flourished long ago in a culture dedicated to a common cause. War not only keeps us from efficiently working together towards this larger goal, it actively works against us in the only fight that matters for life– our fight against entropy. Wars would be viewed as a curiosity of antiquity –being fought over free energy claims by groups of *Homo sapiens* on Earth. This future race of Entropians couldn't fathom how this primal species of human could so blatantly aid in the increase of disorder and human suffering. Entropian morals, reasoning, and collective goals have since relegated warfare to the annals of history.

It's not just the concept of war that's been lost to history. This Entropian culture doesn't even have words in its language for "trash" or "waste". Advanced Entropians with access to vast amounts of free energy recognize that all ordered gradients are sources of free energy in themselves and must not be wasted. To Entropians, all statistically unlikely gradients of physical matter are sources of free energy – as Entropians they recognize their duty to create, steward, and conserve all forms of free energy in the universe.

These future Entropians have mastered the art of using available free energy to create ordered complexity. Not only have they used their vast free energy access to grow the human population, but they have also used this free energy to bring life to billions of other planets in the Milky Way galaxy. They have taken the principles of ecology learned on Earth and spread the wonder of biological life across the cosmos. Along with life, this race creates unfathomable amounts of non-biological gradients. They of course create ordered gradients that benefit human life such as buildings, starships, space stations, and objects that improve the human quality of life. With the free energy Entropians have access to, they could turn asteroids and space dust into entirely new planets, form new stars, and create intricate works of art the size of Jupiter.

Planet Earth was home to the first human Entropians who founded this Entropia. The prodigal use of natural resources, the extinction crisis, and the blight of world wars are all viewed as moral transgressions that luckily didn't last long. The first Entropians are lauded as heroes who found solutions to climate change, brought back species from the brink of extinction, restored natural habitat, instilled a culture of peace and cooperation around the world, reversed our culture of waste and excessive consumption, worked to reduce human suffering through medical advances, and built technologies that helped us colonize our solar system. The first Entropians walk the Earth today and for that, we should all feel a swell optimism for our future.

The entropic philosophy brings us together to work towards a goal bigger than our individual selves. Moral psychologist David Haidt says that we are 90% chimp and 10% bee. This statement is backed up by many evolutionary biologists, including E.O. Wilson, who asserts that our species was shaped by both individual and group-level selection. We humans have what Haidt calls a "hive switch". Religious chanting, cultish corporations, and football games are all things that can activate us to start acting more like a hive and less like individuals. Instead of touchdowns and quarterly earnings, we should start getting hivey about things that really matter. We are most effective, most powerful, and most happy when we work together in a hive-like way towards a common goal and shared belief. The entropic philosophy can help us flip our global hive switch to solve our most pressing and urgent problems.

Unlike ancient religions or antiquated philosophies, the entropic philosophy gives us a schema and set of ethics related to today's most pressing moral issues. Philosophers have been discussing the trolly problem for hundreds of years, but software engineers at Tesla still don't know what ethical code they should write. Enlightenment-era thinkers asserted that we have natural rights that endow us with the right to property ownership. But does this same logic still apply to owning pieces of Jupiter? What did enlightenment thinkers say about owning entire stars or solar systems or galaxies? Even within the last 100 years, Aldo Leopold could not articulate why exactly he felt we should protect wildlife and natural habitats. Leopold himself even said in *A Sand County Almanac* that the reason why the land and biota have value is "admittedly in a state of doubt and confusion". While dogma and philosophy certainly don't mix well, we're in urgent need of a coherent, believable story. Doubt and confusion won't help us with extinctions, climate change, or any other global problem. It's ok for us to be unsure, to stay curious, and to keep searching for truth –

but it's critical that we get some working answers in place as we continue our search.

...

At the beginning of this book, I promised a story, but I'm afraid my story isn't truly an original. Others have told this same story countless times throughout history before me. French novelist Honoré de Balzac told a very similar tale In his 1831 novel, *La Peau de Chagrin* about Raphaël who finds a magic leather horse skin that shrinks every time he makes a wish until the magic skin disappears completely and the wishes run out. More recently, Ted Chiang told the story of *Exhalation*, where he likens our universe's origin to an enormous breath being held. In Chiang's sci-fi tale, the mechanical androids of the future rely on gradients of air pressure to breathe and power their existence. Eventually, all the air pressure in the universe equalizes and all the androids cease to function.

My vision for how the universe began is similar to Chiang's. I've always envisioned the moment before the big bang like an infinite pool of water, raging and torrenting behind the walls of a dam. Eventually, the walls broke, filling our existence with color and supernova swirls of wonder. The entirety of our human existence has taken place in an ephemeral backwater eddy, churning away in obscurity. All of our love, our emotion, torment, suffering, our hopes and dreams, all trapped in a shadowy wisp of current in this great flow of water.

Maybe my biggest unanswered question is if we'll stay trapped in the repeated circles of our swirling eddy – if the current will overpower us and drag us under. It seems that as a species, we're struggling to keep our heads above water. The immense torrent of existence could drown us, but it doesn't have to. I retain hope that we'll learn to swim and eventually break from the confines of the current. When we do, there's a multiverse of new waters out there waiting for us.

Chapter Summary

- We need a new story and as part of this story, we need answers to ancient existential questions.

- Here are some answers provided by the entropic philosophy: We're here as a result of evolution by natural selection in the multiverse to slow the increase of entropy. Our consciousness evolved to allow us access to stores of free energy outside of the niche we originally evolved. We can live a moral life by creating, stewarding, and conserving. We do this by the very nature of our existence. The goal of humanity should be to colonize the cosmos with ordered gradients.

- The laws of thermodynamics forbid the existence of a utopia, but we can still create an Entropia. In this Entropia, humans can live for thousands of years, much suffering has been eradicated, there's no war, and humankind thrives throughout the cosmos.

- What will we do with our consciousness? The choices we make now determine the course of our future.

Afterword

I INTRODUCED THIS book with the disclaimer that these ideas haven't been formally peer-reviewed or published in the scientific literature yet. That said, I have talked individually with academic subject matter experts who don't see any obvious flaws or mistakes with my logic. Time and peer review by experts will tell if the thought experiments in this book hold up or not. Even if an error in my thinking isn't clear now, another future scientific paradigm shift will surely find something amiss. It's the way our pursuit of knowledge has always worked. While these thought experiments provide a great background for the entropic philosophy, they aren't the only reason it could be a beneficial global story.

Even without the multiverse thought experiment, there are other reasons why one might choose to practice the entropic philosophy. The first reason is the same one provided by Robert Lindsay as discussed in Chapter 5. Lindsay points out that life assimilates complexity and order out of random disorder. If this is what life does, then maybe we ought to strive to be the very best at this most basic function of life.

Another reason to practice the entropic philosophy is because it helps ensure the prosperity of future life. Life requires free energy (exergy) to exist. A universe that has reached thermodynamic equilibrium has no free energy left and can no longer sustain any form of life. You don't have to buy into multiverse theory to accept that preserving free energy is something beneficial for us and other potential life in the universe. The grains of free energy are always slipping through the hourglass. If we want to give life in the universe more time, then we need to preserve complex ordered gradients to the best of our abilities.

The very first chapter of this book lays out what I think is the most important argument for the entropic philosophy. We need a new philosophy and we need it soon. We're living through an experiment as a newly globalized society with no real story in place to guide us. The entropic philosophy not only gives us the shared guidance we so need, it also gives us hope for a future without war, waste, extinctions, or disease. In the story of the entropic philosophy, we can be the heroes if we make that choice. We're living our origin story as superheroes right now. The entropic philosophy identifies our villain and sets us on our quest to save the universe. Will we rise to the challenge or continue to squabble in the dirt?

After reading this book, maybe you find this story hard to believe. Some won't like these ideas, but my most fervent hope is that it inspires you to continue your quest to make sense of this existence—to find meaning, purpose, and a worthy goal for humankind. This story is the best I can do for now, but I hope it inspires a new genre of philosophical tales for us to enjoy and choose from.

Acknowledgments

THANK YOU TO Tyler Kaschke for the figure illustrations, cover design, help with pagination, and for putting up with my regular ramblings about life and entropy. For injecting humor and levity into my life otherwise filled with serious intellectual inquiry. For all the meals you cooked, dishes you did, and mundane errands you ran so that I could spend my limited time outside of my full-time job researching and writing. This book really would not have been written without your help and support.

Thank you to Michelle Stampe for teaching me the basics of how to write a book, for providing early developmental edits, and for fielding my questions about the process of writing and publishing. Thank you to Leonard Mlodinow for your mentorship and guidance on writing, publishing, marketing, and becoming an author. Thank you to Michael Price and Lee Smolin for serving as early sounding boards, for challenging my logic, and for helping me improve how I communicate these ideas.

Thank you to my past academic mentors including Brian Smith and Igor Kourkine, who both introduced me to ideas that ultimately lead to the writing of this book. A special thank you to Igor who introduced me to texts on thermodynamics, biology, and economics. The books and ideas you introduced me to had a profound influence on my thinking.

Thank you to my close friends and family for encouraging me to keep going when writing this book on top of a full-time job felt like an insurmountable task. Thank you to my parents and brothers for your interest and support. Thank you to Kelsie Schubick and Amanda Williams for frequently checking in on this project, engaging with me on these ideas, and for always providing support and encouragement when needed. Thank you to Brian Stampe and Justin Newton for showing real interest in these thought experiments and taking the time to ask thoughtful questions. Conversations like these provided me with the much-needed encouragement that maybe others will care about these ideas as well.

I also wanted to acknowledge my employer. My full-time job as a product manager wasn't a hindrance to writing this book in my free time; my gainful employment and all the benefits it provides me is one of the main reasons this book was possible. I'm grateful to my bosses and co-workers for providing a work environment that promotes a true balance of professional work with interests and passions outside my career.

Most importantly, I want to acknowledge all the researchers and thinkers whose work served as a foundation for these ideas. Much of their work is cited throughout this book, but there are countless others too numerous to name. The quip about only being able to see so far because we stand on the shoulders of giants certainly applies here.

Appendix

A Mathematical Analysis of Entropy and Life

THERE SEEM TO be two different camps of researchers; one who claims life is a low entropy system (Schrödinger) and another claiming that life degrades gradients (Schneider). Schrödinger couches the discussion about life and entropy in terms of microstates. These arguments all say that life is lower entropy than non-life because it reduces the number of microstates in a system compared to a system without life. Schneider and others talk about life and entropy in terms of heat. These arguments all say that life creates more entropy than non-life because it absorbs and dissipates more heat than non-life.

Which argument is right? Does life make entropy increase faster or slower in a system? At this point, it's helpful to move away from thought experiments and look at the equations. Specifically, if we look at the equation that relates entropy to heat ($S=Q/T$) and the equation that relates entropy to microstates in a system ($S=k\log W$). Where entropy in both equations has the units of Joules/ Kelvin.

In the first equation (S=Q/T) entropy increases linearly as heat (T) increases. In the second equation (S=klogW) entropy increases logarithmically as the number of microstates (W) increases (a natural log, not a base 10 log is used in this equation). If we stop the analysis here, it looks as though heat has a bigger impact on entropy in a system than the number of microstates.

But once we start looking at examples related to biology, we find that this isn't the full picture. We need to put heat change and microstate change in the context of biological life. For heat change, a generous estimate would be that life runs about 10-20 degrees Kelvin warmer than non-life. This causes entropy to increase in the equation (S=Q/T) by increasing the value of T from ~290K to ~300 K. In other words a 3% increase in temperature and a resulting linear increase in entropy.

Now let's look at (S=klogW). In this equation for entropy, W refers to the number of molecular microstates in a system. W is a huge number not only in the water tank thought experiment, but taking the entire earth as a system. It's difficult for me to even guess at an order of magnitude for the value of W for a tank of water let alone our entire planet, but it's massive.

Life has a huge impact on the value of W in this equation. This is because life creates statistically unlikely complex ordered arrangements of matter out of disorder. Ordered arrangements of matter decrease the value of W on a molecular level by decreasing the number of microstates in the system. Depending on the size of the system you're looking at, this effect could easily be 10 x10^1000 or more.

To summarize, life absorbs and puts out marginally more heat than non-life which causes a slightly higher local increase of entropy. However, life immensely reduces the number of microstates in a system by creating complex ordered molecular structures. If we look at the math, the slight increase of a few degrees kelvin can be made up for, and then some, by the immense reduction in the number of molecular microstates.

With this analysis in mind, it makes sense that a universe would evolve life as a means to store available exergy and preserve gradients, even at the marginal cost of a slight increase in temperature.

Made in United States
Orlando, FL
18 June 2023

34261162R00161